HAUNTED
LIVERPOOL 11

For Audrey Brown

© Tom Slemen 2006

Published by The Bluecoat Press, Liverpool
Book design by March Graphic Design Studio, Liverpool
Printed by Universities Press, Belfast

ISBN 1 904438 35 0

Tom Slemen
HAUNTED
LIVERPOOL 11

The Bluecoat Press

CONTENTS

INTRODUCTION

When Captain Cook's ship approached the Sandwich Islands (now renamed Hawaii) for the first time, in 1778, the ship was invisible to the native islanders because their minds simply ignored it, as they had never set eyes upon such an enormous seagoing vessel before. Their minds were unable to process the information which their eyes were giving them. In a similar way, there is a great deal going on around us that we simply don't see because it is unfamiliar, or outside the mundane sphere of our petty daily lives.

When I was a child I would often peer into a blue summer sky and actually manage to spot the planet Venus, visible as a tiny but well-defined white spot. Few people could make out what I was gazing at and no one believed me when I told them it was the planet Venus. Yet, two centuries before, sailors on the high seas routinely navigated by the position of Venus, regardless of the time of day, be it night or sunny high noon.

The population's eyesight isn't failing, but people's minds, which work in conjunction with their eyes, have become rather lazy and underused, and this sluggish-mind syndrome is at the root of many problems relating to the study of the paranormal. I have personally heard numerous accounts of strange phenomena and lazily remarked, "Oh! That's ridiculous," or "I can't believe that". Doubt creeps in as a safe option when we are confronted with the unfamiliar.

Quantum physics, now widely accepted throughout the universities of the world, was once scoffed at by physicists, and Albert Einstein himself was ridiculed by the scientists in pre-World War Two Germany, who laughingly dismissed his crazy 'Jewish physics' – yet the atomic bomb, which would end World War Two and change the course of world history, was based on Einstein's formulations relating to mass and energy.

Leucippus of Miletus, in Asia Minor, was born around four hundred and eighty years before the birth of Christ, and developed a theory of atoms that was centuries ahead of its time, but fortunately, the hypothesis of Leucippus was not developed to the point where someone realised that it was feasible to destroy a city with just a few small pounds of Uranium 235.

It took until 1933, when a Hungarian scientist named Leo Szilard received an earth-shattering revelation whilst waiting at a set of traffic lights in London. As the lights changed, Szilard conceived the idea of a nuclear chain reaction, and a year later he filed for a patent on his revolutionary concept. The rest, of course, is tragic history.

Believe it or not, humans were not the first to create a nuclear explosion by splitting Uranium atoms; nature did it around two billion years ago in Africa. In 1972, a French physicist named Francis Perrin announced to the sceptical scientists of the world that fifteen natural fission reactors had been discovered in three different ore deposits at the Oklo mine in Gabon, West Africa. These are collectively known as the 'Oklo Fossil Reactors'. Billions of years before the atom-bombings at Nagasaki and Hiroshima, deposits of uranium beneath the soil of Africa had undergone natural fission, yet no one had even discovered the natural nuclear reactors until the 1970s. Had Hitler's scientists known about the uranium isotopes of West Africa, heavens knows how World War Two would have ended.

The belief systems of children are far less constrained than our adult, inhibited and guarded views of the world. The first tale in this book is a case in point, which will test your own open-mindedness to the limit. If you're still under the age of eighteen you may give more credence to the tale than a jaded, logic-led, 'mature' person, although I suspect there are many older readers out there, who, like myself, have never really grown up mentally, and instead have retained a youthful, open-minded outlook on this mysterious universe.

So, open your mind, and read on…

ROMAINE AND THE SHINING MAN

In the 1920s and 1930s, a very unusual private detective, named Alaric Romaine, resided in Liverpool, and had his office at 16 Rodney Street, where the Puschka restaurant is now located. Romaine used highly unorthodox and extraordinary methods of detection, claiming that he was partially telepathic and also that he was able to project his consciousness out of his body; known as Astral Travel to the occultists. Romaine had acquired his esoteric knowledge during the several years he had spent in the company of gurus and yogis in India. Romaine had also allegedly visited many Lamaseries in Tibet, where he had absorbed more arcane knowledge and enlightenment beyond the reach of Western civilization.

Alaric returned a changed man from his tour of the Far East, and decided to use his newly-acquired powers to combat evil and injustice back home. In the sixth volume of my *Haunted Liverpool* series and also in *Liverpool Ghost Walk,* I detailed some of the strange cases which Romaine tackled, and here is one that has never been in print before.

In early October, 1924, a man was going musseling one evening on the sands off New Brighton, when he spotted a ghostly shining figure, running at a phenomenal speed towards him down the beach. As the figure approached, the man realised that the figure was a bizarre entity of some sort, half-man, half-fiend, with outstretched bat-like wings, and a terrifying, evil-looking face out of which shone two dazzling green eyes. The man was so terrified that he dropped his mussel basket, scattering his catch over the sands. Without so much as a backward glance, he ran non-stop to his home, collapsing, breathless, at his garden gate. This was the first sighting of what the locals would come to call 'The Shining Man'.

On the following night, a couple's moonlight tryst was rudely disturbed when they also saw the glowing winged 'man', scrutinising them as he perched in a crouching position, like some huge mythical beast, on a nearby garden wall. Miss Heslin screamed when she saw the unearthly peeping Tom, and her boyfriend also took fright when he too saw the figure. He rushed away from the secluded spot, dragging his terrified girlfriend with him.

A Mr Gosling and a Mrs Flannagan, both in their seventies, were the next to encounter the Shining Man a few nights later, this time staring at them through the window of their cottage in Wallasey village. Mr Gosling rushed outside with a loaded shotgun to give the snooper a piece of his mind, but came running swiftly back indoors when he realised that the spy was not human, but more like the gargoyles sprouting from the church roof, with huge wings and enormous claw-like hands.

The unidentified creature soon had Wallasey village in the grip of terror. Inns and taverns closed earlier than usual, doors were securely bolted, and windows shuttered while the Shining Man was at large. A reporter from the *Wallasey News* set out to investigate and, finding no concrete evidence, declared that if a hoaxer wasn't to blame, then the whole thing must be nothing more than a ghost story that had got out of hand. In the meantime, the Shining Man continued to make appearances in the locality, and a small reward was offered to anyone who could rid the village of the ghastly apparition.

A minister from Rock Ferry performed a special ritual with the intention of banishing what he assumed to be some kind of demon attacking the local population, but instead, he himself became a victim, ending up fleeing from Leasowe Road in a state of abject terror.

It was at this juncture that Alaric Romaine decided to step in and investigate the bizarre sightings, and armed only with his mystical powers and his encyclopaedic knowledge of the Occult, he determined to seek a showdown with the notorious Shining Man.

News about the Shining Man soon spread across the Mersey to Liverpool and on Saturday, 11 October 1924, Romaine arrived at Wallasey village, the scene of the mysterious encounters with the glowing entity which had left the local community living in fear. A corpulent police constable named Wilson was assigned to the job of escorting Romaine to the main area – along Leasowe Road – where the luminous apparition was most frequently sighted. PC Wilson laughed at the idea of the glowing gargoyle with the bat-like wings, but Romaine treated the matter with the utmost seriousness, and as he made his way down Leasowe Road, an October fog slowly drifted in from Liverpool Bay. Within minutes, the two men had become engulfed in a grey void of swirling vapour, and evening was descending fast.

The policeman chatted on about numerous mundane matters but failed to engage Alaric Romaine in conversation. The mystical private eye seemed almost to be sleepwalking as he strolled along with his eyes closed. He led the talkative constable towards the Leasowe Shore, where the fog worsened, and it was here that Romaine snapped out of his apparent trance when PC Wilson suddenly stopped his mindless chatter and called out loudly. Something luminous was floating past them, heading towards the west. Romaine led the way in pursuit of the sinister object, with the puffing policeman reluctantly in tow several paces behind.

When they reached Moreton Common, Romaine and Wilson came upon a horse-drawn caravan parked by a small clump. A dying fire encircled with rocks smouldered nearby and a horse which was tethered to a nearby tree was quietly cropping the grass. The policeman whispered that it was the temporary home of some gypsy folk, which Romaine had already deduced. The detective stood quietly for a few moments before declaring that he could feel a tremendous force being generated by someone inside the caravan, and he climbed the three wooden steps and knocked at the door of the quaint vehicle. The shutters of the caravan window opened moments later, and an old woman looked out at Romaine, who gestured to her with his hand, using some sort of sign language which she seemed to understand.

Then, suddenly, the policeman shouted something, and Romaine turned to see the very apparition that had been terrorising Wallasey Village, hovering directly overhead. The creature looked like some vast, demonic gargoyle, with great, green, luminous eyes and a huge bat-like wingspan. With a flap of its wings it swooped down on PC Wilson, who dived face down into the sand, terrified out of his wits.

Romaine bravely stood his ground, somehow sensing that the winged monstrosity had no real substance and therefore could not harm him and moments later it vanished before his eyes. Romaine was then confronted by another terrifying creature of immense size, with glowing eyes, emerging from the sands as if it had come straight from the bowels of the earth. This creature lunged at the mystic who again stood firm, then passed straight through him, before fading away into the mist.

Romaine then went into the caravan and discovered that all these frightening yet insubstantial creatures were actually projections from the mischievous mind of a twelve-year-old gypsy girl named Laura Horncastle. The human brain contains billions of cells, called neurons, but in the average person, at least two thirds of them lie dormant and unused. Some people develop the capacity to access more of these dormant brain cells – geniuses like Plato, Pascal, Einstein and Edison – whose massive brain power has pushed back the boundaries of science. Perhaps the rapidly developing brain of this young Romany child was also able to utilise more of her dormant brain cells, with devastating results.

Laura, it seems, had an unearthly talent for generating what Romaine recognised as being 'thought forms' – known in the East as 'tulpas'. The girl, being an only child, often resorted to creating imaginary friends and creatures to combat her loneliness. Living in isolation as they did, her only real companions had been an old aunt and a blind grandfather. Romaine had a long talk with the psychic child, and managed to persuade her to stop terrorising the locals with her imaginative 'ghosts'.

The gypsies soon moved on to Wales, and Romaine was rather amused when he later read stories of a 'Welsh Owlman' at large in Aberystwyth!

SCREAMING GINNY

On the night of Sunday, 15 November 1959, a full moon hung over Liverpool, and a gang of schoolchildren hurried homewards in terror from Garston Dock Station, where, despite their mothers' frequent protestations, they had been risking their lives playing on the tracks and railway sidings – until they were confronted by a real-life witch, that is.

In the midst of a savage howling wind which had seemed to blow up from nowhere, a pale-faced young woman with a crooked, disjointed body, long, straggly, greasy red hair and penetrating black eyes had suddenly appeared at the deserted station, and chased the children across the tracks. She had glided down from the platform and on to the railway tracks, from where she pursued them across a scrubby verge of overgrown grass, screaming at the top of her voice.

Jimmy Burns, an eleven-year-old from Island Road, had stumbled as he turned round to see the witch's mouth open wider than should be humanly possible to form a huge, gaping black hole from which came the most blood-curdling, high-pitched screams. Her eyes had glimmered red as she seemed to fly along without moving her legs, which were concealed beneath her flowing black dress.

Somewhere along St Mary's Road, the supernatural pursuer gave up the chase, but the children dared not stop and ran on through the windy moonlit night. Tommy Dinsdale, aged ten, ran panting down Russell Road despite a painful stitch in his side, and was mightily relieved by the welcoming sight of his grandmother waiting for him on the doorstep. He could barely stammer his words out as she chastised him, calling him a gallivanter and a naughty stop out. When he finally regained his breath and told his gran about the screaming witch, she made the sign of the cross and quickly bolted the front door. This alarmed Tommy, and he asked her if she knew who the woman was who had chased them from the old railway station.

As she passed her grandson his pyjamas, which she had been warming by the fire, she declared, in a matter-of-fact way, "Screaming Ginny, that's who you saw."

"Screaming who, Granny?"

Tommy was still on edge and desperately sought some kind of rational explanation for the events of that evening, to put his mind at rest.

"I'm not telling you tonight – you'll never sleep," was all his Gran would say by way of reply and Tommy knew that when she used that tone of voice, there was no arguing with her.

Next morning, in the school playground, Jimmy Burns and Tommy Dinsdale, along with two other boys who had been chased by the demented red-haired harridan, discussed what their parents had told them about the apparition. All the elders' stories seemed to agree, and they all came up with the same name – Screaming Ginny. In addition, all the accounts seemed to match as to why she particularly chose to haunt the railway station.

A long time ago, in the previous century, a strange clannish family by the name of Kneele had moved into an old house in Cressington and a rumour was soon circulating that the family were all witches. Most of the locals shunned the Kneele family and forbade their children to have anything to do with them. Then a succession of neighbours who had shown their dislike for the family began to die in mysterious circumstances.

One of the young daughters in the family, a girl named Ginny Kneele, then fell in love with a local lad named John Reed, who was equally besotted with her. However, when he was told that Ginny was a witch, he became frightened and left her. Ginny tried to put a hex on John to force him to still love her but her mother broke the spell and warned her that she could never marry 'one of them', or she'd lose her powers. Ginny was willing to sacrifice everything, including her supernatural gifts, for John Reed's love, and used all the tricks she knew to bewitch him, but he still rejected her and soon became engaged to a 'normal' girl. Ginny was utterly heartbroken and was quite unable to come to terms with her loss. She could neither eat nor sleep and spent her days gazing out of one of the upstairs windows of the old house, desperately hoping that John would change his mind and come back for her.

One day, the grief and the torment all became too much for her when she spotted John Reed strolling arm in arm with his new sweetheart heading for the railway station at Garston. Ginny followed them on to the platform and there, right in front of her ex-lover and his fiancée, she ran screaming on to the track, where an oncoming train killed her instantly.

For reasons best known to themselves, the Kneele family refused to allow Ginny to be buried in the local churchyard. Perhaps they did not want her to lie amongst those who had rejected her so cruelly in life. So they made their own funeral arrangements and there were even rumours that the witch family had resurrected her body, because the contorted yet unmistakeable silhouette of the girl was allegedly seen at the windows of the house in Cressington – seemingly still waiting for her lover to return.

From that time onwards, her ghost was said to haunt Garston Dock Station – even after it was closed in the late 1940s.

VOICES

O ne busy morning several years ago in Liverpool's Lime Street Station, a man in his early twenties called Simon, was standing among the swarming crowds of rail travellers and commuters, with both hands cupped over his ears. Like the other vagrants and socially inadequate individuals who were attracted to the station, whether it be for the warmth, or simply the comfort of being amongst their fellow human beings, he might as well have been invisible. Most people rushed past him as if he wasn't there, and those who did notice the scruffily dressed young man with the uncombed hair and the stubbly face soon hurried around and away from him, too wrapped up in their own world to have time to stop and worry about anyone else.

For the past five years, Simon had been suffering from a form of schizophrenia. Since his teens he had been a heavy cannabis smoker, and one day at his bedsit on Lark Lane, he was awakened from his drug-induced slumber by a room mate.

"Come on, Simon. Get up, mate. You'll be late for college," he said.

Simon yawned and opened his eyes and looked around the room. There was no one there. Then he heard cackling laughter coming from inside the room. He sat up – no one was there. This scared the young loafer, and he looked around nervously.

"Who's there?" he cried.

"Me," came a voice from nowhere.

"Where are you?" Simon asked.

"In your head, mate. In your noggin," laughed the mocking voice.

And from that moment on, everywhere that Simon went, so did the voice, night and day, day and night. Simon was so disturbed by this turn of events that he eventually sought the help of a psychiatrist, who diagnosed that he was suffering from schizophrenia. Having taken his medical history, it was suggested that the condition might have been brought on by smoking too much marijuana. So Simon immediately gave up the weed, but the tormenting voices stayed with him.

Simon's social life was completely destroyed by the endless chattering voices inside his head. His girlfriend, who he had been seeing for about year, soon abandoned him, because the voices even distracted him during their lovemaking. The voices would laugh and jeer, and come out with the most disgusting obscenities. On one occasion Simon was almost beaten to death as he was watching a film at a cinema on Edge Lane. The infernal voices started arguing amongst themselves until he could no longer follow the film. Eventually he exploded and screamed for the voices to shut up. Two men sitting in front of Simon thought he was telling them to be quiet and they jumped on him outside the cinema and gave him a brutal kicking across the car park.

And now, five years on, he was destitute and homeless, and he slumped into a corner in Lime Street Station and pleaded for the voices to go away as he watched the normal sane people getting on with their lives, going to work and enjoying family life. Then, without warning, a new voice was heard among the usual accents of his invisible persecuters. This new and kinder voice gradually grew stronger and stronger until it actually succeeded in drowning out the evil voices for a time.

"Simon, can I help you?" asked the well spoken male voice.

"Please go away and leave me alone!" Simon pleaded, his hands still pinned to his ears.

"No, Simon. You must listen to me please, I can save you!" persisted the voice.

"How can you possibly save me?" asked Simon, suspecting some new, even more subtle form of torture.

People passing by had no idea of the torment being suffered by Simon. All they saw was a scruffy individual squatting on the floor of the station, gibbering away to himself, and if they did happen to give him a second glance, it was only to sneer at him before hurrying on their way.

"Look over there at that woman, quickly!" the new voice urged him.

"Where?" asked Simon, momentarily removing his hands from his ears and looking about the station.

"Walking towards the escalator, the blonde woman. Do you see her?" asked the voice, suddenly sounding heartbroken.

Simon looked across at the woman. She was heading for the escalator leading to the underground. She was about forty years of age.

"Yeah, I see her. So what?"

"She was my wife," said the voice, a little catch in his voice betraying strong emotion. "I was married to her for fifteen years before I ... before I died ... stomach cancer."

"Why are you telling me all this?" Simon asked, suspicious. "What's it got to do with me?"

He was still afraid that the new voice might really be one of his bad voices playing a trick.

"I want you to give her a message for me," the voice said.

"It's too late now, you've missed her. She's gone down to the underground," Simon told him.

"Well, she'll be back tonight after work, she does the same trip every day. You can give her the message then."

There was an infinite sadness in the man's voice which touched Simon and he sensed that it was not one of his usual tormentors.

Remembering the voice's promise Simon asked, "If I give her the message, how will you help me?"

"I know how the other spirits get into your mind, and I know how to close the way in. They are trying to drive you to suicide because they are determined to get you to join them."

Then Simon's doubts and suspicions returned.

"You don't even exist, you're all in my mind like all the other voices. I'm schizophrenic, that's all.

Simon cupped his hands round his ears again, and felt himself being lifted up by two burly policemen who moved him on out of the station and into Lime Street. But the new voice doggedly stayed with him.

The voice spoke from his left side, saying: "Simon, please believe me, my name is Frank Hughes. I died in ... let me see ... when was it? Three years ago ... I think. There's no time any more where I am, so it's confusing. Anyway, when five o'clock comes I want you to go up to my wife – her name is Hannah – and I want you to tell her something."

Just then a bus on Lime Street sounded its horn and a woman let out a scream. A man grabbed Simon by the arm and pulled him on to the pavement in the nick of time. He had been so distracted by the new voice that he'd drifted blindly into the road.

He swore and cursed the voice, but it somehow managed to calm him down and then told him to go into a red telephone box, which Simon did. It was much quieter in there and the voice spoke once more.

"When you see my wife say, 'Hannah Hughes, your husband Frank still loves you, but you have to move on. He wants you to be happy. Go to David, he loves you so much.'"

Simon borrowed a pen and a piece of paper from a passing student and wrote down the exact words which the spirit of Frank Hughes had asked him to say.

"Simon, the other spirits are very angry," said the voice. " and they're forcing their way back in, but hold on, and don't let them distract you. When I come back, they'll never bother you again."

And sure enough all the same old malevolent, evil, sinister voices came flooding back with a vengeance.

"Throw away that paper now, pretty please," simpered one childish voice.

"I'll kill you in your sleep, Simon, unless you tear up that paper!" threatened another invisible speaker. "Go on! Do it now!"

Simon wandered around the town, into cafés, through St John's Gardens, up and down the high street until finally, at a quarter to five, he arrived back at Lime Street Station, where he was moved on twice by the police. He returned just after five o'clock, and his heart skipped a beat when he spotted the blonde woman entering the station once more. He looked at the paper, and tried to read the words, but the voices in his head sounded like the roaring crowd at a football match. He cursed at them, trying to block them out and re-read the scrap of paper. He started to follow the blonde woman.

"Hannah!" he shouted.

She glanced back, but when she saw Simon, and noticed his unkempt appearance, her pleasant expression changed to one of disgust and she quickened her pace and held on tightly to her handbag, fearing that she was about to be mugged.

"Hannah! Hannah Hughes!" shouted the down and out.

Hearing her full name she slowed down and halted, then turned to face Simon. He hurried towards her and scanned the piece of paper he was clutching, then nervously read out the message:

"Hannah Hughes, your husband Frank still loves you, but you have to move on. He wants you to be happy, so go to David. He loves you so much."

Hannah was speechless.

"How do you know my name? Who are you?" she asked Simon, nervously.

Simon was suddenly overcome with the strangest sensation he had ever experienced. All of the clamouring voices stopped at once, as if someone had thrown a switch inside his head. He felt peculiar spasms inside his mouth, and a creeping numbness in his tongue, as if it had been injected with cocaine, like at the dentist. A powerful force was taking him over. His mouth and tongue moved involuntarily and he spoke in a voice that wasn't his own.

"Hannah it's me, I love you. I've missed you so much," he found himself saying.

Hannah was captivated by this new voice, but she didn't quite know what to make of it. Simon was talking now and yet he didn't have any control over what he was saying. He then found himself all choked up with sadness with his arms around Hannah and before he could really take in what was happening he was kissing her. She angrily pushed him back, screamed, and ran away into the crowds. He fell to the floor, with tears stinging his eyes, yet – he couldn't explain it – they didn't feel like his own tears.

Two policemen arrived on the scene and restrained the vagrant, yet he couldn't properly hear, or understand what they were saying. All he was aware of was a terrible sorrow, and the awful hollowness of lost love, which had taken over his whole being.

Then the kindly voice of Frank Hughes suddenly entered into his consciousness once again.

"Simon, thank you for enabling me hold my wife for that brief sweet moment and for letting me kiss her. It was wonderful to be able to tell her how much I loved and missed her. All that released love has sent those evil voices scurrying away. Have you noticed? They'll never come back again, I promise you they won't."

With that, the voice of Frank Hughes faded away. And as Simon was led off to a police van, he started to smile and then to laugh out loud, because the horrendous, clamouring voices which had tormented him for so long had finally left him in peace.

Those awful voices never did come back, and Simon is now living contentedly in Chester.

THE HALLOWEEN VISITANT

On the foggy Halloween evening of Saturday, 31 October 1874, Father Maurus Anderson of St Peter's Church on Seel Street, was just locking up the place of worship for the night when he distinctly heard a noise outside. He opened the entrance door of the church and directed his lantern out into the swirling autumn fog. The forty-six-year-old Catholic priest heard a low moan, and felt something cold and wet brush past him and enter the church.

He locked and bolted the door then turned, thrusting the lantern in the direction of the invisible intruder. He followed him into the church and lit some prayer candles in order to shed more light on whoever, or whatever, it was that had entered the sacred space for which he was responsible.

Standing erect before the altar, the beloved pastor of St Peter's flock bravely attempted to confront the supernatural visitant. Had he imagined it? No – he knew that it was not his imagination playing tricks when he looked down and saw the glistening wet imprints of someone's bare feet appearing on the floor of the aisle, one after the other, heading in his direction – towards the high altar.

"Who goes there?" he cried, anxiety making the hairs on the back of his neck stand on end.

Father Anderson's voice echoed throughout the deserted church, and he squinted at the faint form before him, materialising piece by piece from a nebulous mist. Eventually, the outline of a young female figure slowly came into focus. Her curly hair was wet through and bedraggled and dripped downwards past an awful dark gash in her throat, and on to the long white gown that clung to her slender body.

"Mary!" gasped the priest, for he immediately recognised the ghost as that of fifteen-year-old Mary Maloney, a poor Irish girl of the parish. She was supposed to be living on a farm in North Wales, not dead in Liverpool, and so terribly mutilated. She stood before him, the tearful dripping spectre of a once beautiful girl who had often called at his presbytery for help. Between sobs she whispered feebly to Father Anderson. It was difficult to make out some of her words, but the priest soon got the gist of what she was trying to say.

Apparently, Mary had been abused and made pregnant by her own uncle, and when he had discovered that she was having his child, he had slashed her throat, then carted her body to the docks and thrown it into the Mersey. During a pause in the ghost's dialogue, a golden radiant light shone out from her abdomen, and the priest could clearly see the glowing image of the unborn baby which Mary had been carrying. The priest blessed the spirits of both mother and child, after which Mary smiled a grateful smile before fading away.

At first light the next morning the priest co-opted the help of two of his parishioners and set off towards the river. They located Mary's lifeless body drifting in with the tide near the Albert Dock. Having been tipped off by the priest, the police raided Bill Morris's Lodging House at Number 82 Melville Place, but Mary's uncle, George Donnelly, had already fled from his room. Donnelly had told Father Anderson only a week before that Mary had been adopted by a farmer and his wife in Wales, when in fact he was merely trying to cover up the dastardly murder of his niece. Donnelly was sighted in Wales a week later, and the police closed in on him, but at the last minute a dense fog blanketed the area and thwarted their efforts to catch him.

However, that was not the end of the story. The following spring, a Welsh shepherd tending his flock on Cader Iris mountain made a gruesome discovery – a rotting corpse, which was later identified as that of George Donnelly. The body was jammed between two crags, badly decomposed and partly pecked away by birds. The murderer was only identifiable from his red hair and several documents which were found in his pockets. He had probably succumbed to a combination of starvation and exposure whilst on the run from the police and had ended up trapped between the crags as he sought shelter from the bitter Welsh winter.

When those who had known both Mary and her uncle heard about the discovery of the body they felt that his death, and the manner in which he died, were poetic justice.

FACE IN THE FLAMES

In October1893, a bizarre money-making scheme was hatched at Number 7 Othello Street, off Stanley Road in Kirkdale. Old Tommy Thompson paid his usual Saturday visit to labourer John Lambert and his family that day, and in the afternoon, under the influence of whiskey-laced buttermilk, he thumped his boot on the floor of the back parlour.

"That's where the money is, my friends. Black gold. It would make you rich beyond your wildest dreams," Tommy told Mr and Mrs Lambert and their three children.

Thompson assured the astonished family that there was a rich seam of coal under the houses of Othello Street. The Lamberts did not question the validity of this outlandish assertion because the old man was much respected in Kirkdale for both the breadth and depth of his knowledge. These were hard times, and John Lambert hadn't worked for an entire fortnight, so the thought of all that coal waiting to be unearthed beneath the terraced house quickly captured his imagination. John's close companion, Edmund Daft, a huge navvy with an iron constitution who lived in Great George Street, was quickly summoned, as was William Corron, another muscular friend of the Lambert family.

On the following day the three men set to work using pickaxes to take up the flagstones in the backyard, and then started digging deep into the soil. By Monday, just as Thompson had predicted, they had struck coal – a huge, black rock of shiny carbonised plant tissue. Some of the coal was soon broken up with the pickaxes and put on the fire which hadn't been lit for a week for want of fuel. It burned gloriously and the three men basked in its warmth. What a find! They might just as well have unearthed a horde of buried treasure.

Lambert soon became carried away, visualising his very own secret backyard coal mine. He planned to undercut the local coal merchants to make a killing, and that day the three labourers also drew up plans for acquiring pit props and other mining equipment which would be transported to the back yard after dark.

However, by the following Wednesday, something very strange had taken place at Number 7 Othello Street. Nine feet down, Edmund Daft had unearthed a huge chunk of coal which was hoisted up in a bucket to Corron, who deftly split it in two with an axe. Inside the coal could be seen the detailed impression of a fossilised fern leaf, beautifully preserved from three hundred million years ago. Shortly afterwards a second chunk was brought to the surface and given to Mrs Lambert to put on the fire. She accidentally dropped it on the kitchen's stone floor, where it broke cleanly in two, revealing yet another fossil inside – a very strange fossil indeed – that of a human face, clearly visible in one half of the broken coal. The impression resembled a death mask with its placid features and closed eyelids.

Mrs Lambert recoiled instinctively from the eerie face.

"How on earth did that get there?" she cried. "It's horrible. I don't like it one bit. Get it out of my house."

But her husband was dismissive.

"It's just a trick of the light, woman," he said. "It'll burn just as well as any other lump of coal and let's face it, beggars can't be choosers. Black gold – that's what I call it."

And without further ado, he shattered the chunk with his small axe, and stacked the pieces in the front parlour's fireplace.

That night, when the fire was lit in the parlour, the coal made strange hissing and whining sounds. Small jets of blue, green and purple flames flickered out of the fire, and Mrs Lambert and her mother-in-law screamed and fled from the house when a man's pale face suddenly appeared in the midst of the flames. His huge, evil-looking eyes stared out at them, and he started to cackle malevolently. The apparition then vanished, but throughout the next week, the furniture in that room was hurled about by some invisible force. Tappings were heard on the windowpanes of the house – even in the upstairs rooms – and when the plug was pulled out of the kitchen sink, a man's menacing low voice was heard talking gibberish as the water spiralled down the plughole.

Mrs Lambert became a reformed churchgoer overnight, and even resorted to nailing horseshoes over every doorway in the house to ward off evil spirits. The poltergeist activity caused such a racket that the police were called in by the startled neighbours. In the course of their investigations into the disturbances, the two constables discovered the illegal coal mine in the backyard. Mr Lambert was prosecuted, threatened with eviction by his landlord, and the hole filled in. The haunting was dismissed as hysteria and no further excavations were ever made under the house to determine whether there were any more three hundred-million-year-old fossils of a human face buried beneath it. If any had been found, it would have made a mockery of current theories of evolution, which state that the first humans to resemble us appeared only two and a half million years ago!

MIRACULOUS CONCEPTIONS

For three years, Tony and Rita Gilchrist – both aged twenty-seven – had tried to start a family, but to no avail. Rita believed that it was she who was infertile, but Tony maintained that it was his 'fault'. In November 1959, the couple – who hailed from the Walton area – were drinking in the Magic Clock pub, which stood on Roe Street in Liverpool city centre, when Rita's friend Maureen, entered the premises. Rita had worked with Maureen for several years at a biscuit factory in Aintree but had lost touch with her almost two years previously, so it wasn't long before the two women were sitting together in a corner of the pub, drinking as they caught up on all the gossip and what was happening in each other's lives. Rita felt a twinge of jealousy when she learnt that her friend now had twin boys, but Maureen had a strange tale about the circumstances regarding the conception of her children.

It transpired that Maureen had also tried to have children for several years without success, until her grandmother, Maude Seymour, had advised her to seek out a certain old bed at a boarding house in New Brighton. It was well known in the area that women who slept in that bed always became pregnant she assured her. Maureen and her husband were both highly sceptical but, like many people in desperate situations, they were prepared to try anything in order to have a child. They searched through most of the boarding houses at the seaside resort, until they finally found the bed described by Granny Seymour. It was an old-fashioned, double-sized bed with a large mahogany headboard which featured three carved heads of curly-haired cherubs. They felt rather stupid believing in such an old wives tale, but nevertheless they booked into the boarding house and spent the night there.

Sure enough, not long after Maureen and her husband had slept in that bed, she became pregnant – with twins. Rita was intrigued by the story and Maureen gave her the address of the boarding house, which was owned by a Mrs Williams. Tony was very scathing when he heard the weird story, but Rita managed to persuade him to give the strange bed a try – they'd got nothing to lose, she argued. The landlady of the lodging house took the prospective customers upstairs to view the bed, and the couple immediately noted the three wooden heads of the angel-faced children carved into the headboard. Rather

22

than feeling reassured, they felt that the cherubs looked decidedly sinister. Despite their reservations, Tony paid Mrs Williams for a two-day stay in the room, then took Rita to the Tower Ballroom where they enjoyed an evening of music and dancing.

When the couple returned, they climbed into the old bed, and Tony soon fell fast asleep. Rita couldn't settle down in the small, damp, claustrophobic room, and she lay awake for a while, before finally drifting off into a light sleep. At around four o'clock in the morning, she was awakened by the sound of children's faint voices and laughter. Then to her horror she glanced to her left, and saw that the carved wooden head of the curly-haired child was no longer looking straight ahead, but now had its face turned directly towards her. The head above her on the headboard was looking down at her, and Rita turned to see that the angelic head to the right of her was also gazing intently at her, and what's more, the mouth of the carving was quivering. Its eyes blinked, and it murmured something which made the other heads chuckle.

Rita let out a scream and pushed Tony out of bed. When he picked himself off the floor and heard Rita's incredible story, he too looked at the spooky headboard and saw the talking, laughing wooden heads. The couple quickly grabbed their belongings and spent the remainder of the night huddled together downstairs in the kitchen until the first light of day, before journeying back to Liverpool.

They had absolutely no expectation of any pregnancy resulting from their brief and unpleasant stay in the boarding house but, several months later, Rita did indeed discover that she was pregnant. Her baby was born with a mop of curly hair, and when he reached his first birthday, not only did he look exactly like one of the cherubs carved into the headboard of the sinister bed, but he also bore an uncanny resemblance to the twin boys of Rita's friend, Maureen.

Alas, Rita and Tony's joy soon turned to sorrow when their long awaited little boy died of meningitis just three years later. Incredibly, Maureen's twins also tragically died in a house fire the same week.

Is this all a case of coincidence, or could the bed in the lodging house have had some unearthly influence on the conception and later demise of the three children?

I recall something similar to the aforementioned tale being reported many years ago in the newspapers when a sizeable number of girls who sat at a certain checkout point in the Asda supermarket in Widnes all became pregnant.

Furthermore, at a supermarket in Kendal, a staggering thirteen women once became pregnant, apparently after sitting at the so-called fertility checkout seat at till number 11. These cases may also have been nothing more than coincidence, or perhaps ... well, who can say?

GHOST AT THE ADELPHI

At 3.30am on the bitterly cold morning of Saturday, 12 November 1927, fifty-two-year-old Arthur Williams, an expert cat burglar from the Paddington district of Liverpool, was on his way home from a disastrous poker game at his brother's house, when he spotted an open window, or as he saw it, an open invitation, on the second floor, on the Brownlow Hill side, of the Adelphi Hotel. From that window, the loud snoring of a slumbering hotel guest reverberated through the still morning air.

Within minutes the experienced opportunist criminal had scaled the face of the building, and upon entering the room via the window, noticed that some other unlikely-looking crook had actually beaten him to it. A girl dressed in a long grey nightdress was rifling through the pockets of the sleeping guest's jacket, which had been carelessly discarded at the foot of the bed. Arthur Williams froze for a moment, wondering if she was the sleeping man's wife, but he quickly dismissed the thought as she seemed much too young. No, she definitely had the look of a sneak thief, he decided.

Arthur emitted an indignant sniff, but the long-haired girl didn't seem to hear him, and failed to turn around. He then glanced over to the top of the bed where the pompous-looking guest with the ostentatious handlebar moustache lay open-mouthed on the pillow, to check that he was still sleeping soundly, before creeping over to the audacious female thief.

"What's your game hey, Missy?" he whispered through gritted teeth.

Arthur stood alongside the girl and realised that she was only aged about seventeen or eighteen. At last she turned to face him, and the burglar's intuition quickly told him that something wasn't quite right about the girl. He tried to push all superstitious thoughts back into his subconscious, but a sixth sense told him that this girl was not alive – she was a ghost. The giveaway was her eyes – they were as black as coal, and as lifeless as a doll's. The girl didn't even seem surprised, and after glancing briefly at Arthur, she resumed rummaging through the pockets of the jacket.

Seconds later, without warning, the girl suddenly discontinued her search turned, and walked straight through the bedroom wall. Arthur gazed, transfixed, at the spot where the girl had vanished into the wallpaper, then heard a faint giggle behind him. He whipped round, and saw the face of the young phantom partially protruding through another wall, inches above the headboard of the hotel bed. Arthur dashed towards the open window and tried to descend to the street, but was so spooked by the spine-chilling incident that he lost his footing and fell awkwardly, sustaining a broken ankle. He was found crawling along the pavement by a policeman gibbering incoherently. He was taken to hospital by ambulance, where he reluctantly related his strange tale to a doctor and the police constable.

In 1954, the same ghostly girl was said to have been seen by none other than the famous cowboy star Roy Rogers and his wife. The American couple were on a visit to Britain when they both succumbed to a bad bout of influenza, and ended up laid up in bed for a few days at the Adelphi Hotel. During the night, Rogers allegedly woke up to find the shadowy form of a girl rummaging around in a trunk, and when the cowboy challenged her, she vanished into thin air.

Winston Churchill reported seeing the very same apparition during a stay at the hotel a few years before, and in the 1940s, the American film star Robert Montgomery – then a serving naval lieutenant – actually chased the spectral girl down a corridor at the Alelphi, during a party, and watched her vanish into a wall.

The identity of the Adelphi ghost, and why she searches through guests' belongings, remains a mystery.

HIGGELDY

Around the year 1910, Margaret Harrison, a widow from Liverpool, came to stay at the house of a relative on Wellington Road in New Brighton. Mrs Harrison also brought her two daughters, twelve-year-old Elizabeth and nine-year-old Mary Ann – known affectionately as Polly – to the seaside house in the autumn, in an attempt to try and rebuild her life after the tragic death of her husband John, who had died from a fever whilst undertaking a transatlantic voyage. Mrs Harrison's cousin, Bessie Evans, was herself a widow, and her health had been in decline of late, so she had invited the family into her spacious home for a period of rest and recuperation, and she hoped that their company would also help her to overcome her loneliness.

The girls settled down well within days, and enjoyed playing on the nearby sands and exploring the old seaside caves along the rocky coastal outcrops known as the Red and Yellow Noses. One evening, just after the children had been put to bed, Mrs Harrison heard a strange noise echoing faintly through the house. The Liverpool widow left the parlour with a candle and went to investigate where the peculiar noise was coming from and she soon discovered that it had originated in the cellar. When she opened the door to the cellar, she saw to her surprise that it was completely flooded, and that in the far right-hand corner there was a long hole in the wall where many of the bricks had apparently given way.

Then she saw something that would haunt her for the rest of her life.

Two shiny black hemispheres – resembling upturned glazed bowls – were protruding from the rippling dark water, and as the widow lowered the candle to determine exactly what they were, she realised that each of the domes had a dark yellow eye. Mrs Harrison let out a strangled scream, and the eyes instantly dipped beneath the water and vanished. The widow's legs turned to jelly, and she was barely able to stagger back out of the dark basement to alert her cousin to the thing that had invaded her basement.

When she found Bessie, she babbled incoherently about the hideous creature with the yellowish eyes, and then collapsed into an armchair, trembling from head to toe. Instead of sounding surprised, Bessie just nodded and gave her a knowing look. She told Margaret not to worry, that she'd simply seen something that had been living in the flooded cellar for many years – 'Higgledy' she called it – some sort of sea creature, apparently. Over a cup of tea Bessie told how her mariner husband Henry had tried to catch the thing with all manner of bait and traps, but the slippery creature had always managed to evade being captured. It came and went as it pleased, via an opening in the cellar wall which led to a tunnel, which, in turn, ran to the shore, and over the years she had grown used to it. Depending on the height of the tide, the cellar was usually under six to eleven feet of water.

The previous occupant of the house – a mysterious and rather eccentric individual – had allegedly fed the tentacled creature with all manner of living things, ranging from rats and chickens to his own dog! Bessie chilled Margaret to the marrow when she described how Higgledy, as her husband called the thing, once emerged from the water and revealed itself to be some sort of giant black octopus with staring dead eyes and a huge pointed beak. Her husband had fired a revolver at the creature and it had quickly submerged itself under the murky cellar water. It can't have been seriously harmed because it had continued to inhabit the waterlogged cellar. The children overheard the talk of the terrifying marine animal, and the daughters became hysterical at night when they could hear Higgledy splashing and thrashing around in the basement, perhaps hunting sewer rats.

Not surprisingly, the Harrisons soon decided that they had stayed long enough at the seaside house and, making polite excuses, they returned to the safety of their Liverpool home. The unidentified octopoid creature was never captured, and as late as the 1950s, there were rumours that it still visited the flooded cellar on Wellington Road.

THE ANGELS OF MONS

In August, 1914, the British Expeditionary Army was forced to retreat from the German onslaught in the disastrous aftermath of the Battle of Mons, on the Western Front. Grey hordes of advancing Germans could be seen as far as the eye could see, and two soldiers – Williams from Liverpool and Yates from a small Cheshire farming town – were assigned to a party forming part of the rear guard. The two young men accepted that they were staring death in the face, but courageously acknowledged their duties without question. The thunder of the German artillery was getting closer by the minute, and shells squealed above their heads and exploded nearby, leaving no trace of the retreating soldiers and cavalry horses who had been in their path.

"Terrible weather, Yatesy," joked Williams, grimly, and he and his comrade instinctively ducked down as a shell blasted a piece of the British artillery into lethal pieces of flying scrap metal just a few hundred yards away. Row after row of grey uniformed men poured forward, seemingly without end, and Williams opened up with the machine gun which Yates helped to feed – until the ammunition ran out, that is – then they had to rely on their single rifle shots, which were woefully inadequate in the face of the enemy's superior firepower. It was true that several Germans fell as a result of their efforts, but there were always more to replace them. All around them was death and destruction. Even the massive rats which had plagued them in their stinking trenches were now lying dead or dying.

The Liverpudlian and the Cheshireman fixed their bayonets in readiness for the final confrontation, and listened to the chilling crackle of revolver fire as the German officers shot their own young deserters who were turning around, weary and shell-shocked, unwilling to submit to becoming fodder for the bullets and shells which were peppering their ranks from the thin green line.

"This is it!" said Yates, and made the sign of the cross.

The Liverpool lad smiled wanly, and for some unknown reason, cast his mind back to his old schooldays. He remembered his old history teacher, Clarkey, and how he had thrashed him into learning Latin. What was that Latin phrase old Mr Clarke had drummed into him? That motto that you were supposed to quote when all hope was lost? Yes! That was it! 'Adsit, Anglis, Sanctus Georgius' – St George help the English.

The Liverpool man gritted his teeth and recited the Latin phrase over and over again as if this mantra could somehow influence the outcome of his dire situation. He started to shout it to the darkening skies, as the smoke and dust thrown up by the pounding shells turned day into night. Yates cupped his hands round his ears to try and make out what he was reciting, as shells obliterated the landscape all around him, sparing nothing.

"What are you going on about?" Yates called to his crazed companion. "I can't hear a word that you're saying."

He was convinced that Williams had finally succumbed to shell shock, like so many others from his regiment.

"St George deliver us!" Williams shouted. "By the English blood in my veins, save us in our hour of need!"

Suddenly, right along the front line, strange luminous beings, some eight feet in height, seemed to surge up out of the ground. The German cavalry halted in its tracks. Their horses whinnied and fell down dead, as did the soldiers who had rushed forward with bayonets fixed. Turmoil and chaos reigned as the German advance ground to a halt. The Great General Staff thought that the British must have released poisoned gas, for the German dead bore no wounds, just expressions of abject terror on their contorted faces.

The so-called 'Angels of Mons' stood their ground until the retreating British were safely out of harm's way, before vanishing back into the gloom. When the news of the spectral army reached London, armchair generals were quick to blame the incident on battle fatigue, but the returning soldiers swore that the angels were as real as the horror from which they helped them escape, and the miracle proved to be an enormous morale booster for the British troops.

Williams, the man credited with summoning the angels by his appeals to St George, died in Liverpool in the 1950s.

A Twisted Tail

If you walk down Liverpool's Church Street and turn right into Tarleton Street, you will come across a pub called the Carnarvon Castle. Today the street forms part of a pedestrianised area, but once upon a time, when Tarleton Street was still cobbled and full of horse-drawn traffic, there were eight public houses to be found along its length.

The Carnarvon Castle is very popular today, and in the 1880s, the snug little public house was just as regularly frequented. In the year 1881, three regular drinkers could usually be found propping up the bar at the pub, and they were Harry Woolwright, Jack Mercer and Danny Donovan. Harry wore a patch covering a vacant eye socket, and had a shock of white, upright hair with a dark streak through the centre parting. Jack was the youngest, a mere lad of nineteen, with curly coppery red hair and a round full face. Danny completed the distinctive-looking trio. He was bald on top with two black clumps of hair on each side of his head, and a pair of the most vivid, striking blue eyes you have ever seen, which many women remarked upon.

Whenever they congregated at the Carnarvon Castle, these three men passed the time singing, arguing, waging bets and getting up to all sorts of tomfoolery. They sang songs in perfect harmony, in the manner of the barber shop vocalists, and as closing time loomed at the Carnarvon, Harry, Jack and Danny could usually be relied upon to give a beautiful rendition of *Londonderry Air*, which has the same melody as *Danny Boy*. Rory O'Callaghan would provide the backing music on his accordion, and the performance invariably brought a tear to the eyes of the weary drinkers at the pub.

In December 1881, an Arctic blizzard swept over the town, blanketing the streets with a deep layer of pristine snow. An elderly, strange-looking gypsy woman who had been selling heather and hand-carved clothes pegs outside of St Peter's Church, took refuge against the snowstorm in the Carnarvon Castle, and she was accompanied by three black, dishevelled-looking cats.

Harry, Jack and Danny immediately started making fun of the Romany woman's long aquiline nose and her scruffy cats, and three times the old gypsy warned the men that she would blight their lives with an evil spell if they did not stop their harassment. Harry Woolwright, the eldest of the trouble-making trio, was certainly old enough to know better, but in a deplorable show of cruelty, he kicked one of the old woman's cats into the fire, and the poor creature screeched in agony from the appalling burns it sustained, and it died soon afterwards.

The old gypsy woman pointed an arthritic, twisted finger at Woolwright, and let out a venomous curse in some strange, ancient dialect, which seemed to be comprised of a mixture of arcane Greek, Persian and Armenian words. At the same time, the two remaining caterwauling felines arched their backs against her long apron and bared their teeth at Harry and his mocking friends. Then the Romany woman suddenly collapsed, moaning before gasping for air and making the so-called death-rattle sound, which is often heard in elderly people just before they are about to expire. The pub instantly fell silent and even the three jokers ceased their barrage of insults. Within minutes, the Romany woman was dead, and several drinkers doffed their hats out of respect.

Soon afterwards, Harry, Jack and Danny realised that something peculiar was happening to them. All three of them clutched at their throats and began to cough. They complained of an irritating feeling at the back of their throats, as if there was hair stuck in them. They soon became so short of breath that they had to leave the pub and go back to their homes to recover from the strange symptoms. The three men were not seen at the Carnarvon Castle for over a week – an unheard of length of time – eventually returning to the pub shortly before Christmas. Other Carnarvon regulars who had known Harry, Jack and Danny for several years began to notice a strangeness in the men's behaviour. Their eyes darted about as they stood at the bar, and instead of breaking into song at every opportunity, each of them would hum nervously in a low voice without opening their mouths. Furthermore, the trio spent the evenings constantly checking the pub clock, and would leave well before midnight, even if someone had just bought them a drink.

On Christmas Eve, a policeman named Bulman was welcomed into the Carnarvon Castle. He took off his cape and removed his snow-flecked helmet, before being warmed by a generous measure of Scotch – courtesy of the landlord. The policeman entered into conversation with Danny Donovan and Jack Mercer, but the two men barely paid any attention to what he was saying and just kept glancing at the pub clock.

At precisely ten minutes to midnight, they prepared to leave, along with Harry Woolwright, but the jovial constable barred their way and insisted upon them finishing their drinks. Young Jack Mercer became very agitated and rudely told the officer of the law to get out of his way. PC Bulman was offended by the youth's disrespectful attitude, especially when he had just bought him a drink. Jack then shoved the policeman out of the way and struggled to undo the bolt on the pub door. The policeman drew his truncheon, suspecting that they were up to no good, but Danny Donovan and Harry Woolwright seized the constable by each arm and hurled him into a group of startled drinkers who were sitting round the edge of the bar. The three men then fled from the pub into the snowbound streets.

"What on earth's got into them?" asked the barman.

"Damn cheek!" snarled PC Bulman. "That's gratitude for you! I'm sure they're up to something."

Trying to regain as much dignity as he could, he picked himself up off the floor, donned his cape and helmet, and hurried out of the Carnarvon Castle in hot pursuit of the impertinent trio.

There had been yet another snowstorm that night, but it had finally fizzled out, and it was an easy matter for PC Bulman to follow the three trails of footprints in the virgin snow, and he soon noticed that they were leading towards Church Street. When he reached St Peter's Church, the policeman noticed something very strange indeed. The footprints of the drinkers' shoes in the snow had abruptly been replaced by cats' paw-marks. He was more than a little spooked by this, but the biggest shock was to come shortly afterwards, as he shone his bull's eye lantern down a dark corner of nearby Church Alley.

Five feline eyes reflected back the feeble torchlight – three were green and two were bright blue. They were making melodious meowing sounds, which sounded just like *Londonderry Air,* arranged in a familiar harmony. PC Bulman cautiously drew nearer to the alley cats, and saw that one cat looked just like a feline representation of Harry Woolwright, in that it only had one eye, and had a dark streak down the centre of its snow-white head. The other tomcat looked utterly outlandish, because it had a pink bald patch which stretched from one ear to the other, as well as a pair of vivid, striking blue eyes. The third, round-faced cat was of a deep coppery red colour.

The unpleasant chill that ran down PC Bulman's spine had nothing to do with the frosty night air. It had slowly dawned on him that through some sinister, supernatural means, the three singing cats he had just seen had been none other than the three ne'r-do-wells, Harry, Jack and Danny just minutes ago. Unable to take in and make sense of what he was seeing, and unwilling to stick around to seek an explanation, the policeman returned to the Carnarvon Castle and downed two neat whiskeys, one after the other. He decided to say nothing about the strange incident back at the police station, probably because of the fear of losing his job, for who would believe such a ludicrous tale?

The three men returned to the pub days several later, and the other drinkers in the Carnarvon Castle soon became very suspicious of their uncharacteristic behaviour. Mary Sullivan, a local prostitute, having watched the trio nervously eyeing the clock, concluded that they were leaving the pub at a prearranged time for criminal purposes – and being an inquisitive person, she trailed after the three men.

As the three drinkers walked into the shadows of Manesty's Lane, their forms seemed to shrink, as some kind of unbelievable metamorphosis took place. Mary squinted into the darkness, unable to believe what she was seeing. Where three men had walked just seconds ago, three cats now silently pussyfooted along in the shadows. Mary let out a shriek and flew back to the Carnarvon Castle, and pounded on its bolted door. She was finally admitted by the barman, and when he and the other drinkers heard the prostitute's uncanny story, there were a few uneasy, hollow laughs, but several of the drinkers remembered the old gypsy woman's cursing of the three men and intuitively knew her story to be true. An old man in the pub named Ted Sarson said he had witnessed such a Romany curse take effect years before in Cheshire, when a lord who had evicted a band of gypsies off his land was turned into a werewolf. From that time onwards, every night as darkness fell, he would sprout hair on his hands and body and prowl around the countryside on all fours.

When Harry, Jack and Danny returned to the pub on the following night, they immediately descended on the bar, and when the three men started arguing between themselves over some matter, old Ted Sarson quipped, "Keep the noise down there will you, fellows? You're arguing like the Kilkenny cats."

All eyes in the bar sheepishly turned towards the three men, and Rory O'Callaghan began to play his accordion over in the corner seat in order to break the embarrassing silence, but on this occasion, Harry, Jack and Danny didn't seem moved enough to sing along with the street musician.

It is said that months after this, the body of young Jack Mercer was fished out of the Mersey, and a grotesque tale circulated, telling how, in the form of a ginger cat, he had been seized by the neck by a watchman's dog at the docks one night and hurled like a rag doll into the river. By first light the drowned cat had mysteriously been transformed back into its human counterpart and was found bobbing up and down in the swirling murky waters of the incoming tide – as dead as a dodo.

What became of Harry Woolwright and Danny Donovan is not known, but there were tales of Danny fathering a child who also inherited the terrible curse. If that is true, perhaps somewhere in the city tonight, after midnight, strange cats will be out on the prowl ...

COFFEE TABLE COFFIN

In 1957, a forty-six-year-old draughtsman by the name of Frank Moorcroft, entered a red telephone box in Birkenhead, and called his wife June, who was at their home in Huyton. Frank was about to embark on an affair with Shirley, a secretary from his work, and he knew that his wife already had grave suspicions about the nineteen-year-old typist, but he had always reassured her by saying that he had no interest in the girl whatsoever.

So, on this particular day, Frank pretended that he was in Widnes on business, but his wife June was still suspicious.

"Are you sure? I hope you're not with that little trollop," she said, with grave misgivings.

Frank gave a false laugh.

"Course not," he lied. "You've just got a very suspicious mind, that's your trouble."

However, something he hadn't bargained for soon gave the game away. As he lied to his wife, the One O'Clock Gun was fired from the Morpeth Dock nearby, and June was a very perceptive woman, with keen hearing. She had originally lived in

Cleveland Street in Birkenhead, and she had heard the One O'Clock Gun being fired each day throughout her childhood. It was a six-pounder, naval, anti-aircraft gun, and was fired each day as a time check signal for ships' chronometers.

"You're a liar, Frank," she said. "You're over the water in Birkenhead. That was the one o'clock gun."

"What are you talking about?" said Frank, lamely. "That was a car backfiring."

"I'd shut up if I were you," snapped June. "You're just digging an even deeper hole for yourself.

"But ... but ..." stammered Frank desperately trying to think of a way of defending himself.

"But nothing," snapped June.

She then called him a liar and a cheat and hung up.

Frank certainly felt like a low-down cheat, and instead of spending lunchtime at his secretary's flat as he had planned and been looking forward to all week, he boarded the ferry back to Liverpool, and went home to try and make peace with June. But June dismissed his grovelling apologies and was not in the mood for forgiveness. Flinging a few things into a suitcase, she set off for her mother's house after saying that they should have a trial separation.

After a week of being on his own, Frank Moorcroft's guilt had changed to anger and when a friend at work said that he would set him up with a blind date he agreed to go. And so he found himself one Saturday at noon, standing under the statue on Lewis's corner, feeling uncomfortable and decidedly foolish; he was too old for this sort of thing, but he wanted to get back at June and at first this had seemed like such a good idea, but now he wasn't so sure. He felt that everyone was staring at the red carnation in the lapel of his Mackintosh, advertising the fact that he was on a blind date. What a cliché and what an idiot he had been to agree to the date in the first place. What if one of his friends should pass by? He could just imagine the comments he would get at work on Monday if anyone found out.

He was supposed to be waiting for a woman named Lily whom he'd never set eyes on before. At around twenty past twelve, a beautiful-looking woman of about thirty turned up at Lewis's Corner, and she waited there, blushing slightly, looking just as uncomfortable as he was. After some ten minutes had passed, Frank wondered if this vision of beauty could possibly be Lily. Perhaps this date wasn't such a bad idea after all! Plucking up courage, he turned to her, and at that same moment she turned to him.

"Lily?"

"Jim?"

"No," they both said simultaneously, feeling ridiculous.

They both stood there, awkwardly, checking their watches, and it soon became clear that these two lonely people had both been stood up. Frank at least saw the funny side of his predicament, and ended up saying, "I'll be Jim if you want."

The woman grinned and put a gloved hand to her mouth, then smiled and said, "And I'll be Lily."

Frank then introduced himself properly, and the woman told him that her name was Edith. Frank suggested going to the Vines pub on Lime Street, but Edith told him she would prefer to go to a café, as it was far too early in the day to start drinking.

Frank walked Edith to his car, parked just off Renshaw Street, and they drove to Capaldi's Milk Bar on Smithdown Road. At the milk bar, Frank explained how he was recently separated from his wife, and Edith said that she had been in a long-term relationship with a man called Mike until he had committed suicide a few years back. Frank offered his condolences and asked what the circumstances were. Apparently, she and Mike had been a happy loving couple until a young woman had started seeing him in secret. This woman then dropped Mike and he was so overwhelmed by the break-up, that he had deliberately crashed his car into a wall and killed himself. As Edith told Mike about the tragedy, she had a wild, almost insane look in her eyes.

Later on, at around 7pm, Frank and Edith went to a few pubs and ended up at one called The Majestic, on Hall Lane, near Kensington, where, it turns out, Edith lived. This was an era when people would still drink and drive, and no one thought anything of it, as unbelievable as it sounds today. A policeman on his beat actually helped Frank Moorcroft into his car outside the pub, and bade him goodnight.

Frank drove Edith to her home off Molyneux Road. Having been invited in for a nightcap he slumped into a comfortable sofa, and she turned on a soft lamp, and put a bluesy album on the record player, then snuggled up next to him. In the middle of the sitting room was a strange, long coffee table, about twenty inches in height, and around five and a half feet in length. Over it was draped what looked like an old chenille curtain. Frank's shoe accidentally kicked against this box-like coffee table, and he noticed that it sounded hollow.

He soon found himself passionately kissing Edith, and then, all of a sudden she announced that she was going to bed, and promptly left the room. Frank grinned to himself, this was definitely his lucky night, this would show June! So he got ready to go upstairs after her, but as he did so the record on the turntable became stuck, and he went to turn it off. As he walked towards the record player, his leg again bumped the side of the long, covered coffee table. He looked down, and out of curiosity, pulled back the curtain which was draped over it. It wasn't made of wood but of glass and inside …

"Oh! My God! What the …"

Frank's heart turned somersaults inside his chest and he felt faint and light-headed.

Under the curtain was a long glass case and lying inside the case was the body of a badly decomposed woman. Her skeletal features still had bluish patches of skin attached to them, and her rotted eyes had sunk back deep into their bony sockets.

He steadied himself on the arm of the sofa, but before he had time to think, something hard had smashed into the back of his head, and his brain seemed to explode in a blinding flash of light. His knees buckled and he slumped to the floor from where he looked up to see Edith standing over him wearing nothing but some skimpy underwear, and in her hand she wielded the long metal stand of an ashtray holder. Frank somehow managed to clamber to his feet by pulling himself up on the furniture, when she clubbed him again, this time blinding his left eye with blood. This made him see red and summoning every ounce of strength he managed to push her on to the sofa, then quickly groped his way into the dark hallway. Miraculously he managed to unbolt the door and unfasten the lock, then he stumbled into the street, shouting for help.

A succession of passers-by assumed that he was drunk and ignored his cries for help. So, in desperation, he hammered on a neighbour's door and as he did so he saw Edith running off, half naked down the street, screaming like something possessed by the devil.

The police soon caught the woman and took her into custody, where she was assessed by a psychiatrist who had her committed her to a mental hospital. Further investigations revealed that the corpse in the upturned glass fish tank was that of the young woman who had caused Edith's boyfriend Mike to kill himself. Edith has since died and it is said that the house in Kensington where all this took place is still haunted by her ghost and that of the woman in the coffee table coffin.

LETTER FROM BEYOND THE GRAVE

In December 1923, the body of sixty-seven-year-old Mrs Heath lay in an open coffin in the front parlour of her home in Nevill Street, Southport. Wreaths of evergreens gemmed with roses lay in the hall, and upstairs in the bedroom, Moira, the forty-year-old daughter of the late Mrs Heath, was being comforted by her close and lifelong friend, Anthony. Moira was so beside herself with sorrow that, at the last minute, she couldn't bring herself to attend the funeral, so Anthony volunteered to stay behind and look after her.

As the hearse slowly carried the coffin away to the church, Moira and Anthony stood at the bedroom window, watching it turn the corner, past the Coliseum Cinema, and into the depths of a swirling fog, followed by the entourage of mourners.

The house was hushed and empty now that the black-clad friends and relations had left, and Anthony and Moira sat before the blazing coals of a roaring fire in the drawing room, each sipping a sherry as they reflected on the life and personality of the deceased woman. Moira had mixed emotions about her dead mother – she had loved her dearly but resented her constant interference in her life. She told Anthony that if it hadn't been for her mother's constant interfering, she would still be married to Douglas, and would have had children around her now to comfort her in her hour of need. Alas, Mrs Heath had put such a strain on her daughter's relationship with Douglas, that he had divorced her fifteen years ago. Now she was left on the shelf, condemned to live alone for the rest of her life.

Moira was wallowing in self-pity when Anthony suddenly said, "Look, Moira, that's all water under the bridge now, love. You've got to get on with what's left of your life and make an effort to build a future for yourself."

"How can I, with so many awful memories? Mother has ruined my life!" she cried, starting to sniffle.

"Look, I know this might sound a little bizarre, but I was reading a book on psychology the other day, and the author mentioned this very interesting case ..." Anthony was saying, when he was interrupted.

"Not now, Anthony, please."

"Wait, Moira, please hear me out," Anthony went on. "A man blamed his mother for giving him some psychological complex which had blighted his life.

37

I think she dressed him in girl's clothes when he was a child, or something similar. Anyhow, the psychiatrist told the man to write a letter to his mother asking him why she had given him a complex with her bizarre antics – even though the man's mother was dead."

Moira frowned.

"What good would that do if she was dead?"

"You see, just the act of writing the letter had some sort of therapeutic value for the man, and his complex gradually disappeared," Anthony explained.

"So, are you seriously suggesting that I should write a letter to my mother?" Moira asked.

Anthony took some time to persuade his bereaved friend to write the letter, but in the end she succumbed to his pressure, and that evening she sat at her late mother's Davenport writing desk, pouring her heart out on to the paper. Anthony sealed the letter and 'posted' it inside the Davenport's drawer. He advised Moira to now forget about the letter and to accompany him on a winter break to Scotland. Moira gladly took up the offer and thanked him profusely.

"You really are the dearest friend, Anthony. I don't deserve your kindness."

And she smiled for the first time since her mother's death.

At Guthrie Castle, a week later, after a couple of stiff whiskeys, Anthony produced a ring and on his bended knee, shocked Moira with a proposal of marriage. He admitted that he had loved her for so many years, but had been too shy to ask her to marry him, for fear of rejection and the loss of her friendship. Moira accepted the proposal without any hesitation and flung her arms round him.

"Oh! Anthony! You are the most wonderful man I've ever met. Of course I'll marry you."

The newly-engaged couple arrived back at the house on Nevill Street, and some time later, Moira noticed an envelope on the Davenport writing desk when she was dusting in her mother's room. Inscribed upon it in a familiar script, were the words: 'To Moira'.

Moira opened the letter, and almost fainted as she scanned the contents of the letter. It was a reply to the letter she had written to her late mother. The handwriting was without question that of her mother, and unfortunately, so too was the acidic, scathing prose. The author of the letter accused Moira of being a trollop, and claimed that Anthony had taken advantage of her during a time of crisis so that he could marry into her wealth.

'But not over my dead grave!' the letter ended.

Then a faint chuckling sound was heard nearby. Moira ran screaming downstairs and fled to Anthony's house. At first, Moira's fiancé thought the letter from beyond the grave was some kind of sick joke, but soon appreciated how deadly serious Moira was about the matter.

Whenever Anthony visited the house on Nevill Street, supernatural incidents would occur. A wine glass was hurled at him by some invisible hand, and on one occasion, when he fell asleep embracing Moira on the sofa, he was awakened by a pair of ice-cold hands trying to throttle him. Moira also caught fleeting glimpses of a woman in a long black dress wandering about at night in her bedroom, and could even detect the distinct aroma of the perfume her mother used to wear.

Shattered nerves eventually got the better of Moira and Anthony, and they ended up moving away from Moira's family home to Birkdale. When the wedding finally took place, not only did a substitute ring have to be used because the wedding band had vanished from the best man's pocket, but the interfering ghost of Mrs Heath even put in a personal appearance at the ceremony. This happened just as the priest was intoning that part of the marriage service which asks: "If any of you can show just cause why this couple may not lawfully be married, speak now, or else forever hold your peace."

An agonising shriek that seemed to originate in the transept echoed throughout the church. Some of those gathered for the ceremony later said that they had briefly seen a woman in black, shaking her fist at the couple, seemingly in protest at their union.

Fearing repercussions from the interfering ghost, Moira and Anthony subsequently moved even further away, to Ormskirk, and were troubled no more by the vindictive dead relative.

THE NUN IN THE WALL

In 1971, thirty-five-year-old Nelly Blackstock decided to try and start a new life for herself. She had separated from her husband the year before, because of his serious drinking problem which he refused to address and which was making her life and that of her children, a misery. Nelly and her fifteen-year-old daughter Joanne and twelve-year-old son Martin, were now staying with her at a house on the outskirts of Liverpool. I am not at liberty to say where this house is because it is still standing and people are living in it – but the house dated back to the 1920s.

Nelly, like a lot of women in a similar position, was curious to know if romance would ever come her way again after the break up of her marriage, and a week before Christmas, in 1971 she travelled to Liverpool city centre to consult a fortune teller called Mrs Berry, who had a consulting room on Bold Street. Mrs Berry sat her down and put her at her ease then peered into her crystal ball in the darkened room. Before long she began to speak.

"An older man is going to come into your life, Nelly. But beware! This man has a dark secret concerning a woman. Do not be deceived by his kindness. He is not to be trusted. He is a wolf in sheep's clothing."

"Can you see a name in the ball, Mrs Berry? A name would help me avoid him." The fortune teller looked deep into the crystal ball.

"I see you sitting down to dinner with this man, who may be called George, either in name or surname. It's a candlelit dinner and there are two children eating with you. A boy and a girl."

Mrs Berry described the two children, and Nelly recognised them as her own children, Joanne and Martin, but she was puzzled by what she had just heard.

"That seems a bit odd. How would I be having a candle-lit dinner with a man – with my children at the table? That's not very romantic, is it?"

Nelly was getting rather irritated, Mrs Berry wasn't making much sense, and she was beginning to regret ever coming, when the fortune teller suddenly recoiled in horror.

Nelly nearly jumped out of her skin.

"What ever is it?" she asked. "What can you see?"

"I see a woman in black, a hooded woman – just a silhouette – she has long since died but never crossed over. She's in the wall – she's in the wall."

An uncomfortable prickling sensation shot up and down Nelly's spine when the fortune teller said that.

"What does that mean?' she asked.

The clairvoyant ignored her question but gasped, her knuckles showing white as she clutched the crystal ball with her bony hands.

"I see a funeral hearse, with you inside the coffin, my dear. Be warned. If you stay with this man, he'll kill you."

The session was over before Nelly had time to quiz Mrs Berry about the stark warning she had just been given. She left the premises on Bold Street in a total daze and made her way home consumed with dread. The fortune teller's predictions constantly preyed on her mind and ruined that Christmas.

However, early in 1972, Nelly met a lovely man named John Gee, who had a cottage in the suburbs of Huyton. He was an older man, but thankfully his name wasn't George, so, albeit rather cautiously, Nelly started a relationship with him and she gradually regained her confidence. For the first time in years she was enjoying being a woman.

They had been seeing each other for some weeks when one night there was a power cut – just as Nelly was in the middle of cooking an evening meal for herself and her boyfriend and Joanne and Martin. Parts of the National Grid had been cut off to conserve energy because of the coal miner's strikes. Despite the power cut Nelly managed to cook a meaty stew, followed by apple crumble and custard, all made using the gas cooker. They all ate together by candlelight and the children enjoyed the novelty. Afterwards they played the card game Rummy until bedtime.

The children stayed in separate rooms that night, and Nelly slept with John Gee, and she told him about the fortune teller Mrs Berry and her dire predictions and about the woman in the wall. John Gee seemed quite shocked by what she had told him, but made no comment. Nelly had expected them to make love that night, but he said he didn't feel well and turned away from her.

At around one o'clock in the morning screams were heard coming from Martin's room. Nelly and her daughter rushed into the room to find the lad in a highly distressed state, quivering under the blankets. He had left the candle burning at his bedside, even though Nelly had told him to blow it out before going to sleep. Between sobs, Martin told his mother that a woman in black had slowly come out of the wall, her arms reaching out for him. Her body was horribly broken and disfigured, and blood had been gushing from her nose and mouth.

"I think she was some kind of nun, Mum," shivered Martin, clutching her tightly.

Joanne had also been woken by the commotion and she too was upset and clung to her mum and young brother. At this point John Gee came into the room and tried to reassure Martin that he'd only had a nightmare, but as he spoke the shadow of a woman glided across the wall and the candle spluttered and went out.

Nelly and her children screamed in unison and blundered out of the room.

They could hear John Gee swearing and using obscene language as if he was cursing someone behind them in the dark room. Then they heard a woman's voice wailing.

Even though they were all in their nightclothes, and it was a freezing cold night, Nelly and her children dashed to the front door of the cottage, desperate to get out. As Nelly struggled to take the top bolt off the door, John Gee appeared at the top of the stairs and turned on a powerful flashlight, aiming its blinding beam straight at her. In an instant he was at the bottom of the stairs where he grabbed Nelly by her long hair and started to swing her violently round the room. Joanne and Martin were both terror stricken by now. John Gee's face was pure evil, contorted in the torchlight, and he raised the hefty torch and struck their mother on the head. This triggered Joanne into action. Adrenalin coursed through her veins as she grabbed an old ornamental flintlock which was hanging on the wall, then yelled out in fury and struck John Gee on the back of his head twice. He turned around, smiling lopsidedly, and Joanne screamed, fearing that he would now attack her, but his eyes rolled up into his forehead and he crumpled up with a thump.

Nelly and her children still couldn't open the door – it had been locked and the key hidden – so they had to scramble out of the window. They walked for what seemed like miles through the ice and snow in bare feet, until they found a telephone box. Nelly had just dialled 999 when she was relieved to see the headlights of a car slowing down on the road outside. Relief turned to horror when she saw John Gee's crazed, blood-stained face gazing into the window of the telephone box. He was wielding what looked like a huge hunting knife in his hand. They were trapped in a living nightmare that seemed to have no end. Joanne and Martin started to cry, but Nelly kept her wits about her and shouted down the telephone for help. She told the emergency operator that their attacker was outside the telephone box at that moment, armed with a knife. The operator told Nelly to hold on, the police would be there in a very short time.

The three of them tried desperately to keep the door shut by pulling on the handle, but John Gee managed to prise it open – his rage had given him superhuman strength and nothing was going to stand in the way of his murderous rage.

"You don't know why I did what I did," he mumbled incoherently, wild-eyed, with spittle forming at the corners of his mouth.

He stood there for what seemed like an eternity, brandishing the knife, and rambling on without making any sense. Throughout her ordeal, Nelly bravely tried to shield her children from this madman who she had allowed into their lives. Then, without warning he thrust the knife at her arm, drawing blood.

"I've got to do this, but I don't want to," he ranted.

At that moment the headlights of a car came down the road, and Nelly shouted, "Here are the police! Leave us alone!"

But it was just a delivery van – which drove on past.

Like a mad dog Gee grabbed Nelly by the arm, and tried to drag her out of the box, but her children held her back. He became even more enraged, and seemed intent on slaughtering all three of them there and then in the phonebox. Then came the sound of a distant screech of tyres and sirens blaring. A police jeep came careering round the bend in the lane, and squealed to an abrupt halt ten yards away. Then followed another police car, and then another. John Gee turned and froze in the headlights of the police cars. He flung the knife into a snowdrift, and made a dash for his car, but he slipped on the hard-packed ice and fell heavily on to his face. Two policemen piled on top of him and handcuffed him as he snarled and spat like a wild animal. Meanwhile two other officers came to the aid of the traumatised family who were still cowering in the phone box.

John Gee – real name Arthur George – was later jailed for the sickening assault and knife attack, and the court dismissed the story of the ghostly woman in black as an hallucination born of the demented mind of Arthur George, who had a long history of psychotic illness. But this does not explain why Martin had woken in terror having seen a woman emerging from the wall, or why the three of them saw the same woman gliding through the room when John Gee, alias Arthur George, came through the door.

Nelly later heard disturbing rumours about that cottage in Huyton, which is now surrounded by houses which have been built since the 1970s. According to these rumours, George had either killed a nun, or perhaps run her down by accident in his car, and had concealed the corpse in a niche in the wall and then bricked it up. People who lived in the house have seen what they describe as black orbs on photographs taken in the house, and complain of an uncanny feeling after dark – the feeling of someone watching them …

Perhaps some poor soul out there reading this book tonight lives in that house, and is unaware that they have the body of a woman hidden in their wall.

REMEMBER THE CHILD

A ngry masses of snow-laden clouds loomed low over Liverpool one glacial afternoon in February 1959. At a house on Livingston Drive, within a stone's throw of Sefton Park, a crotchety man of sixty-five, Frederick Kingston, was hunched in his high-backed armchair in front of a miserable fire which he had only lit a few minutes before. He sipped from a mug filled with rum and milk, and had his feet planted firmly in a bowl of mustard-clouded water – an old remedy for a chill.

Kingston was at war with everyone: his neighbours, the charlady who came to clean up his home, the voices on the radio, the faces on the television screen. Nothing and nobody escaped his scathing criticism, and he knew deep down that when his time came, no one would miss him. Old Kingston's deepest resentment was reserved for the children who, in his opinion, played too loudly in the street outside, and on that snowy Saturday afternoon their excitement levels had hit an all-time high. It seemed that every child in the neighbourhood was either building a snowman, tobogganing, or throwing snowballs, all accompanied by loud squeals of delight. When two snowballs thudded against the window of his cosy parlour, Kingston became so enraged that he stepped out of his mustard foot bath, screaming profanities, intent on giving them a piece of his mind. But he was in such a rush that he tripped over the rag rug and crashed to the floor, painfully cracking his head on the coal scuttle. The bang to his head left him with concussion.

Kingston's nephew Chad was given the unenviable task of looking after him while he recovered, but he accepted the challenge quite cheerfully. However, days into what seemed like his good recovery from the fall, Kingston began to act – and sound – decidedly odd. Chad was surprised, to say the least, to come upon his Uncle Fred twirling round an imaginary skipping rope in his bedroom one morning, and when he asked the recuperating elder what he was doing, Fred replied in a childish voice,

"I'm skipping, of course. Come on, Chad, skip! It's fun"

Later, Fred got dressed ready to go out and informed his bemused nephew that they were going to play in the park. The worried Chad suggested that calling a doctor might be a better idea, but Uncle Fred laughed, and in a child's voice, said he'd never felt better than "on this lovely sunny day". Fred then bounded out of the house with Chad in hot pursuit.

As he followed his unhinged uncle from the house, the winter sun's rays finally broke through a dense low line of oppressive clouds. With a curious spring in his step, Fred headed for Princes Park, jibbering excitedly to unseen companions whom he referred to as 'Bobbo' and 'Tillymint'. From the juvenile nature of the conversations, Chad established that the two invisible characters of his uncle's imaginings were probably his childhood friends. Chad was acutely embarrassed by the indignant looks of a succession of passers-by who had to move quickly out of the way to avoid being tripped up by the frolicking pensioner.

Beneath the snowy mantle of Princes Park the unborn flowers of the coming spring were hidden from sight, yet in the eyes of ten-year-old Fred Kingston, signs of summer were already all around. Kingston was obviously experiencing the park of his childhood, long ago, when the long hot summers seemed to last forever and the park was their kingdom from morning till night. He stroked his old friend Judy the park donkey, and later laughed loudly as Tillymint – the nickname of younger sister Mary – trotted towards him on the long-lost, long-eared friend.

In the midst of all this childish jollity, Fred suddenly became faint and dizzy and had to be helped to a park bench, which his nephew cleared of snow. In that moment, the long hot summer of 1904 was cruelly replaced by the cold empty present, stretching before him to a lonely grave. In the white limbo of the park, Kingston found himself clinging to the gravestone of that little donkey, who had given her last ride for children in 1920.

"I was young once, you know. I really was," the old man muttered with rheumy tears blurring his eyes.

"Come on uncle, you've had a nasty fall and you should be indoors on a day like this. Let's get you back in front of that nice fire."

"You're a good lad, Chad," said Kingston.

Fred Kingston's youth had lain buried in the past, and the passing years had almost obliterated his recollections of those halcyon days, until the fall and ensuing concussion had somehow rekindled those golden cherished memories of his boyhood.

From that day on he has never again hated children – he has envied them instead.

WHERE A THISTLE GROWS

The Scottish town of Ullapool, nestled on the shores of Loch Broom, with the majestic mountains of the Highlands as a backdrop, has to be one of the most beautiful places in the world. In the 1890s, sixteen-year-old Caitriona Ferguson, a beautiful but poor Ullapool girl, regularly used to meet up with her seventeen-year-old sweetheart, Robert MacGregor, at a trysting place in the Highlands. Caitriona – or Katie as she was more familiarly known – dearly loved Robbie MacGregor – he was her first love – but he had no ambition in life. Being an orphan, with no one to care for him, he had turned to poaching and stealing, and lived in a cave during winter and under canvas in the summer, all of which Katie disapproved.

One hot May afternoon, the two young lovers lay among the heather, and Katie was contemplating her future as bees murmured lazily among the celandines, primroses and meadowsweets, and, of course, the glorious purple thistles. Robbie lazily presented his sweetheart with a Melancholy Thistle, which has no prickles on its stem, unlike the normal thistle.

"'Tis like me," said Robbie. "Looks as if it could hurt, but has no thorns. I'm like that; all bravado and fighting talk, but I couldn't harm anyone."

Katie held that thistle to her bosom as if it were a single red rose. But she was a practical girl who did not let her emotions run away with her. She turned and confronted Robbie and told him that he would have to work honestly if he truly desired to become her husband. Robbie took the criticism badly – he had to scrape a living as best he could with no parents to support him – and he stormed off in a huff. Katie was upset by his reaction but was not prepared to retract what she had said.

The weeks wore on and Katie received no word from her lover. Then a thirty-year-old photographer from Liverpool named Stephen Hastings came to the Highlands in search of picturesque scenes for his portfolio. He was tramping over the moors one day lugging with him his heavy photographic equipment, when he came upon the beautiful maiden Katie Ferguson walking through the heather, deep in thought. He stopped in his tracks, bowled over by her beauty. This was one of those rare cases of love at first sight.

After spending many weeks at Ullapool, Stephen invited Katie and her mother Una to come back with him to Liverpool, and they gratefully accepted the invitation, never having been to a bustling port like Liverpool. Robbie MacGregor was devastated when he learned that his beloved Katie had gone off with a man to a city far away, and, consumed with jealousy, he swore that he would go and bring her back. He was held back by a wise old man named Finlay, who informed him that Liverpool was nearly four hundred miles away and he might get there and find that she refused to see him. Better to wait and let Katie's heart decide what was best for her.

"She may have a change of heart, Robbie, so leave it in abeyance for a while," was the old man's advice.

Robbie took his Skean Dhu knife from his stocking and threatened to kill the Sassenach Hastings, but as soon as the knife was in his hand he realised that they were just empty words. He couldn't hurt a fly. He was indeed like the thistle with no thorns and tears came to his eyes as he had remembered that day in the heather.

Katie had been swept off her feet by the Liverpudlian and by mid-July she was engaged to Hastings, and a spectacular wedding was planned for the Spring. However, early one morning, Katie was wandering alone in the large walled garden of her fiancé's home, when she noticed a lone thistle which had sprouted up amongst the English flowers in the herbaceous border. Instantly she was transported back to Scotland and that day in the heather when she had cut Robbie to the quick with her sharp words. A tear trickled down her face as she realised what she'd done. She still loved Robbie, more than Stephen Hastings, more than anyone in the world and she broke off the engagement that same day, despite her mother's protestations. Stephen Hastings was heartbroken but she stood firm, despite feeling deep pity for him.

When Katie returned to Robbie at their old trysting place, he cried unashamedly and hugged her tightly to his chest. They both vowed never to leave each other again. He conceded that she had been right to criticise him – she deserved better – and he soon gave up his no-good ways and obtained a job at the local mill. He married his sweetheart a year later – and all because of a humble thistle.

THE CIRCLE OF LIFE

*This life you now live goes round in a never-ending circle. When
you die you will go back to the beginning and live it all over again.
Every pain, every joy, every thought, every incident, small or great
in your life shall be experienced again. The eternal hourglass of
existence is turned over and over, and you with it, a grain of dust.*

What you have just read was the view of the controversial nineteenth century German philosopher Friedrich Nietzsche, defined in his theory of 'Eternal Recurrence'. Could there be any truth in Nietzsche's theory, which makes a mockery of the old saying, 'You only live once'?

For centuries, the tantalising phenomenon of déjà-vu – which means 'already seen' in French – has been experienced by people from all walks of life. It usually manifests itself as a sudden feeling that something which is apparently happening for the first time, has actually happened before, and the person experiencing it even knows what's going to happen next.

I have experienced the baffling phenomenon of déjà-vu many times in my life. Many years ago I was drinking in the Waldeck pub, when I suddenly 'knew' that the barmaid was going to pick up several empty beer glasses, to put in the frontloading glass washer, but that they'd all slip from her hand and smash at her feet. The barmaid collected the glasses, and as she went to put them in the sanitising machine, they all fell from her hands and crashed at her feet sending slivers and shards of glass flying everywhere.

On another occasion, I was walking through St John's Shopping Centre, when I suddenly knew that a girl I had not seen in almost ten years would come around the corner in front of me. Seconds later, the very same girl appeared from around the corner of a shop, and I was struck dumb.

I received a letter from a woman named Marie a few years ago, who told me of a curious case of déjà-vu, which was somewhat different from the usual type, in that Marie actually told a friend what was going to happen – and it did. The incident took place at the Pier Head one stormy January day in 1976.

Marie was walking hand in hand with her boyfriend Chris at the Pier Head when she suddenly had a powerful sense that everything that was happening had happened before. She knew exactly what Chris was going to say before he spoke, and, more alarmingly, she also knew that the landing stage was about to sink. She frantically told Chris to get away from the waterfront because an unusually strong gust of wind was about to hit, but her boyfriend just gave her a quizzical look and dragged her, protesting, down the sloping corridor to the landing stage, telling her not to be so ridiculous. Marie grew increasingly agitated. The sensation of impending disaster was so strong that she suffered a panic attack and ran back up the corridor in fright. Chris was concerned by her behaviour and raced after her.

Moments later, a tremendous gale-force wind blew up from nowhere and battered the landing stage. Massive waves rose up from the Mersey and swamped the floating platform – and it soon started to sink. A couple of people who were stranded on the landing stage just managed to scramble to safety in the nick of time. Chris was deeply shocked by what had happened. How could Marie possibly have known that that wind was going to arrive and that it would sink the landing stage?

He eventually caught up with Marie near the Cunard Building, and she told him that the feeling of déjà-vu had already faded. This was a relief for the young woman, as the faculty of knowing the near future had proved to be a terrific strain on her nerves.

Is déjà-vu a case of the mind somehow circumventing time and glimpsing the future – or is Nietzsche's theory of Eternal Recurrence correct – and have you read these very same words many times before in your previous lives?

MR KNAPPLE

It all began one Saturday afternoon in November 1951, when, for reasons unknown, the swings in a playground in Paddington had been chained up to prevent anyone using them. Perhaps the Council had decided they were unsafe. Anyway, a frustrated gaggle of children from nearby Kinglake and Highgate Streets looked for a new focus for their play. They soon wandered off towards the Botanic Gardens on the borders of Kensington and Wavertree, in search of amusement on this grey Saturday afternoon. The children climbed the walls in the park and started pelting one another with dry sods of soil which exploded into clouds of dust upon impact. The toothbrush-moustached park keeper hated any kind of disorder in his park and he chased the five children out of his territory and on to Edge Lane.

The children took flight down Beech Street, and threaded their way down an alleyway which opened out into a deserted court. Here, something terrifying took place. Little seven-year-old Joan Fletcher, the only girl in the gang, was idly gazing at the top of a six foot tall yard wall, when she saw something peep over the top of it. It was a small, hawk-nosed face wearing a jester's three-pointed hat with faintly jingling bells hanging from each point. The odd little figure, which was obviously a puppet, waved a small Marotte – a sceptre topped with a miniature jester's head.

A voice behind the wall asked, "Hath anyone seen the witch?"

Almost immediately, another puppet – that of an old hag in black with a pointed witch's hat – rose over the top of the wall, brandishing a broomstick. The children smiled at the out of place puppet show, and stood there, spellbound as the witch and jester battled one another on top of the wall. After about ten minutes of this odd spectacle, Bobby Roberts, the leader of the gang, started to climb the wall in an attempt to see who the puppeteer was. He was just about to haul himself over the top when the jester puppet was withdrawn from the play. Then an unusually large white hand, with long, tapering fingers emerged from behind the wall and grabbed Bobby's scarf. The boy let out a strangled yelp as the hand then tried to drag him over that wall. He screamed and kicked furiously and eventually managed to extricate himself from the clutches of the bony hand and ended up falling to the ground as his scarf slid over the other side of the wall.

Bobby and the other children ran off, but couldn't resist returning to the wall a few minutes later; their childish curiosity overcoming their fear. They just had to know who, or what, was hiding behind that wall. An agile boy named Terry scrambled up and walked along the top of an adjacent wall and saw something that chilled him to the marrow. Clearly visible were the puppets of the jester and the witch being manipulated on top of the wall – but no hands were visible, and no puppeteer was present – as if a ghost was working them.

Stunned by what he had just seen, Terry almost toppled off the entry wall, but he managed to regain his balance and scrambled down. The gang again ran off in fear when he told them what he had just seen. As they careered off down Edge Lane they bumped into a policeman walking his beat.

"Steady on, lads. What's the rush?" he asked, stopping them in their tracks.

"Sir, sir!" they all gabbled at once.

"Steady on, one at a time. You all look as if you've seen a ghost."

"We have!" panted Terry. "Come and have a look if you don't believe us."

"Go on then. Lead on."

The policeman could plainly see that the children were in deadly earnest and he followed them to the wall where he too saw the weird puppet show being performed. To the children's surprise, he revealed that he had seen the puppets himself on that wall many times over the years, and added that the ghost of a Victorian puppeteer named Mr Knapple, who had lived at the house which belonged to the yard wall many years ago, was often seen working the puppets. He always wore a top hat and had a long pale face. Apparently it was well known in the neighbourhood that this puppet master had gone insane after the death of his sister in the late Victorian period. Not long afterwards, Mr Knapple had committed suicide by hanging himself in his attic, which was also his puppet workshop.

The policeman and the children watched as the puppets slowly sank back below the wall, as if their puppeteer knew that he was being watched and had decided to end the show. A window cleaner later saw the top-hatted ghost of the puppeteer standing in the yard with the puppets still in his hands. Seconds later, the figure had faded away.

One member of the children's gang, a boy named Georgie Jackson, suffered terrible recurrent nightmares after his encounter with the ghostly puppeteer, and even today, he still shudders at the mere mention of Mr Knapple.

MEET ME AT CAPALDI'S

The five grey, secular days of the working week were over, and now, at last, it was the sunny Saturday morning of 23 July 1955. Frank Hughes, a Liverpool draughtsman in his late forties, entered Capaldi's Milk Bar at 266 Smithdown Road and was soon enjoying a coffee and a cheroot in a window seat. At precisely 11am he looked over the top of the morning newspaper he'd been perusing and beheld the pleasing sight of Marie Cunliffe crossing the road outside, heading for the milk bar. He jumped up and courteously opened the door for her, and she leaned towards him on her tiptoes.

Her kiss, plus the Evening in Paris perfume she wore, almost overwhelmed Frank, and her shapely form turned the slicked heads of two immaculately attired teddy boys seated at a corner table.

It was obvious from the sparkle in the eyes of the twenty-five-year-old cinema usherette that she brought good news.

"He died this morning at eight!" she tried to whisper, but she couldn't contain her excitement and most of the customers in Capaldi's overheard everything she said.

For two long years Marie had lived with Roy Cunliffe, her sick, fifty-year-old Irish husband, and for the whole of those two years she had been seeing Frank behind his back. And the secret joke the couple shared was that Frank was Roy's best friend.

"Ain't that a shame?" sniggered Frank, callously singing the title of the popular Fats Domino number, then hugged Marie. Now he could buy the brand new Ford Zephyr he'd been promising himself, and take that holiday to Texas he had always dreamt about, all paid for courtesy of the small fortune Roy would leave to his beloved wife Marie in his will. No more secret rendezvous at milk bars and seedy all-night cafés; no more sneaking about. Now Frank and Marie could show their love for the whole world to see. Life suddenly looked very rosy indeed for the conniving couple.

Roy Cunliffe was laid in an open coffin in the sitting room of his house, and the wake commenced. His shameless widow Marie was comforted by her sister and, of course, Frank, as well as a host of sympathetic friends and neighbours, who persuaded her go to the local pub – "It'll take you out of yourself, love" – where she put on an Oscar-winning performance as the grief-stricken widow.

Marie ended up getting quite drunk that night; people were falling over themselves to buy her a drink – "It'll help you to drown your sorrows, love," – and when she returned home, her sister prepared supper for her before going to bed.

"Are you sure you'll be alright now, Marie?" she said. "Is there anything else I can get you?"

"No thanks, you get to bed. Frank will look after me. He's a good mate is Frank," and she turned to Frank and gave him a wicked little wink.

"Okay then, if you're sure you're alright. I must admit I'm dog tired. See you both in the morning then. Sleep well."

"Yeah, you too."

When Marie was sure that her sister was safely tucked up in bed she snuggled up to Frank on the sofa. She giggled as she told Frank that her late husband had regularly dabbled with an ouija board, which she had always treated with the utmost contempt.

"Let's have a go with it for a bit of a laugh, shall we? Let's see if Roy Boy's got anything to say for himself."

Still in a tipsy state, she brought the board into the parlour and set it down on the coffee table. She then convinced Frank to join her and put his fingers on the upturned glass on the ouija board. Marie immediately felt the glass sliding about the board and she quickly took her fingers off it as if she'd been given an electric shock.

"You're pushing it," she said to Frank. "Stop it!"

"No, I'm not. Look!"

Frank took his hand off the glass – and it kept moving all by itself! What had started as a bit of a laugh had suddenly turned nasty and he felt a horrible lurching in the pit of his stomach as the glass slowly spelt out the word, 'ADULTERY'.

Frank and Marie both sobered up in a flash and exchanged guilty glances.

"Oh! It's all a load of nonsense anyway," said Marie, trying to appear nonchalant, but she was visibly shaking.

All pretence that everything was alright soon evaporated when the coffin containing Roy's body suddenly started to shudder and jerk. The couple's terrified screams filled the parlour. Then the coffin slid off its stand and landed bolt upright. The white shrouded corpse of Roy Cunliffe was flung out of the coffin, and its cold, clammy bulk landed squarely on top of Frank Hughes, who squirmed with revulsion.

"Get it off me! Get it off me!" he screamed. "I can't breathe!"

Then the lights went out.

When they came back on, Frank was clutching his chest and gasping for air, doubled up in agony. Roy's body was lying beside him, eyes wide open. And was that the hint of a smile on his livid white face?

From that day onwards Frank was plagued with heart trouble, his health ruined. Marie too suffered a nervous breakdown and finally came to see the error of her ways. She admitted to a priest that she had committed adultery with Frank Hughes behind her dying husband's back and was relieved to get the whole matter off her chest. The parlour was later blessed and the accursed ouija board thrown away.

A WINDOW INTO THE PAST

The territory of time is almost beyond human imagining, when one considers how long this planet of ours has been in existence. Present estimates say that our world is 4.6 billion years old, but even that seems tame in comparison to the age of the universe itself, which is estimated to be some 20 billion years old. On the grand scale of the universe, our precious lives seem like a microsecond of consciousness in the infinite time-space continuum of the Cosmos.

During that brief span of life, we spend a third of our time on earth asleep, and, according to mystics like the great Armenian freethinker George Ivanovich Gurdjieff, even in our so-called waking state we are in a type of daydreaming trance most of the time, as we read books, newspapers, magazines, text inane messages, watch television, and listen to music on the radio or MP3 players. We tend to live solidly in the here and now, and regard yesterday as gone and tomorrow as something which has yet to arrive, even though quantum physics has shown scientists that all time is eternally present and our perception of time is incorrect. We think of time as being linear, that we are moving along a line like the needle on the groove of an old gramophone record. The stylus is the present, the groove behind it is the past, and the groove ahead is the future. Yet we know that the entire list of songs of that album is on the whole of that vinyl record, all of them existing at the same time, even though it may take forty-five minutes to play the songs with the stylus.

Einstein and other scientists have long established that time is a fourth dimension of space, and that, incredible as it seems, all of the events of the past, the present, and the future, all exist at the same time. Our consciousness and limited mind creates the illusion that time is passing by, when in fact, it is our perception which generates the deception. In other words, our consciousness is like the needle on the record, and how the music it plays seems 'live', when in fact it is a recording.

These intriguing laws of quantum physics mean that right 'now', the Beatles are playing lunchtime sessions over at the Cavern, Liverpool Castle is still standing in Derby Square, and seagoing dinosaurs are swimming in the tropical waters of Liverpool Bay. Of course, to visit these events we would have to be able to travel through this fourth dimension, which is the point at which our scant knowledge lets us down. Nevertheless, some scientists have been brave enough to draw up blueprints for nuts-and-bolts time machines. Go to Google and key in 'Frank Tipler' to see what I mean.

There is also an intriguing possibility of time-travel being accomplished by projecting the mind beyond the prison of the present in a way similar to the astral projection techniques used by remote viewers. I have personally experienced several timeslips, and know that time-travel is a reality, but my concern is that the military powers of this planet will meddle with historical events, for example to ethnically cleanse nations currently regarded as enemies of world peace. I have often wondered if some time traveller could journey back in time to snatch Hitler as a baby and allow him to be reared in a different environment, thus preventing six million people from perishing in the Holocaust. The flip side of this is the possibility of some future Neo Nazi journeying back to the 1940s to give Hitler's military scientists the plans of a hydrogen bomb to be dropped on Russia and delivered to America on the type of Super V2 rocket Werner von Braun was working on.

Passing through the time barrier is smoother than you think, and it can happen in the most unlikely of places.

In 1979, a manager looked out of the window of his Church Street office in Liverpool during his lunch-break and encountered a spectacle which shocked him to the core. What he saw was the Church Street of what seemed like Victorian or Edwardian times, with horse-drawn omnibuses, hansom cabs, men in top hats and bowlers, and bonneted women in ankle-length dresses. The manager yanked opened the door and screamed downstairs to his business partner, who came scuttling up to the office wondering what on earth could be the matter. He looked out of the window and he too saw the amazing scene of bygone Liverpool being played out in the street below, and he urged his friend to go outside to find out what was going on. A fear of the unknown prevented the manager from venturing downstairs; he found the whole affair unnerving, but his partner bounded down the stairs, intending to step into the milling crowds of quaintly dressed people.

However, the scene beyond the second-floor office window soon changed back to the mundane Church Street of the present day. The men knew that it was impossible for them to have shared the same hallucination, yet they were at a complete loss as to suggesting an explanation for the baffling incident.

When the mechanisms of timeslips are properly understood, they will open up the past to historians in a way that is difficult to imagine, but sadly, like everything else that is discovered, timeslips will probably also be used for a military purposes, or for the benefit of individuals rather than mankind.

HAUNTED CHILDHOODS

One of my favourite poets is William Blake (1757-1827). He was a mystic, a visionary, a painter and an engraver, and at the age of four he allegedly said that he saw God looking in at him through a window. From that moment on, Blake looked forward to the day of his death, when he was convinced that he would step into the world of spirit.

At the age of nine, young William saw a host of angels in a tree with bright angelic wings bespangling every bough like stars. No one believed him, of course, but William doggedly maintained that these spectral beings were actually there, as real as the stars in the sky. Even in his mid-forties, Blake was still seeing things which no one else could see; angels descending from the heavens on a ladder, for example, and strange luminous goings-on in his garden, which he took to be a fairy funeral.

Of course, it's easy to regard Blake as a fantasist; a man with a mental or personality disorder who has lost touch with reality, but there are many otherwise sane and level-headed people from dustmen to astronauts who have also had mystical experiences during their childhoods. However, unlike the famous poet, they have repressed, rationalised, or simply forgotten these hazy memories of infancy and youth, as they do not fit comfortably into their adult perception of the world.

In my case, many vivid and valued memories of strange incidents from my boyhood are still fresh in my memory. Recollections of a strange olive green bird which would fly down into the half-demolished ruins of an old house on Melville Place in Edge Hill are one example. In this case it definitely wasn't my youthful imagination working overtime, because my uncle and grandmother and many children on Myrtle Street also saw this strange bird as well. One mischievous boy from Myrtle House seemed fixated on trying to catch the bird, with no success.

My uncle and his neighbour decided that the peculiar looking bird was a parakeet, but a bird expert in the neighbourhood disagreed and would sit at the window of his flat in nearby Myrtle Gardens, watching the mysterious winged creature through a pair of small binoculars. He even sketched the bird, and I noticed that its head resembled that of an eagle with prominent ears, rather like the mythological Griffin. The green bird of Melville Place stopped visiting after the ruins of the house were finally swept away by bulldozers.

A reader's recollection of a strange childhood incident takes us a little further back in time, to the 1950s in Bootle.

In 1956, seven-year-old Joan Kenning and her six-year-old brother Jimmy used to visit their grandmother at her home on Downing Road, Bootle, and she would regale them with scary tales of bogeymen, fairies and hump-backed hob goblins as they sat around the fireside of her old house.

One evening the grandmother caught Joan and Jimmy snooping about in the pantry, and warned them not to eat the green, marble-veined cheese which was lying on a plate on one of the shelves, as it would cause them to have terrible nightmares. Of course, childhood is all about doing exactly the opposite of what your elders tell you not to do, and so, predictably, Joan and Jimmy sneaked out of bed after hearing their granny's deep snores coming from the next bedroom. They made a beeline straight for the pantry, their mission – to sample the 'nightmare cheese'.

"I bet she was just pulling our legs," said Joan, breaking off a piece of the forbidden cheese.

"Yeah! I bet she doesn't want us to have any 'cos she wants it all to herself," said Jimmy. "Give us a bit."

The greeny-blue-veined cheese tasted delicious, but Joan was careful to only slice off small pieces of the mouldy, highly seasoned cheese, so their Gran wouldn't notice what they'd been up to.

What a grave mistake it proved to be. At around three o'clock in the morning, Joan woke up, drenched in sweat and quaking from a terrifying dream which she couldn't quite recall. When she sat up in bed, she was astonished to find that the other end of the bedroom seemed to be about three hundred yards away. The room had taken on the aspect of a long corridor, and at the far end of this elongated room, two eerie, bizarre-looking figures approached, accompanied by faint music.

Moments later, Jimmy woke up with a yelp, and winced as he too saw the same two figures in the distance, at the end of the impossibly stretched room.

They were a man and woman, dressed in outdated clothes and impossibly stretched as if they were wearing stilts. The man, in a black, hammer-tailed coat had legs that were at least ten feet in length, and the woman's bell-shaped dress concealed legs that must also have been nearly as long. The disproportionate figures waltzed to the music, and as they got nearer, the frightened children grabbed hold of one another. The 'stretched' man kicked up his long, stick-like legs and screamed with laughter while the music played in triple time. The woman twirled and cavorted about, also screeching with laughter. The waltz is supposed to be danced sedately, but this pair turned it into a manic, whirling jig which terrified the children.

Today, Joan describes the weirdly distorted couple as looking like they had stepped out of one of the paintings of the Spanish artist El Greco, only they were even more elongated than the painter's usual subjects.

The children were soon at their grandmother's bedside, shaking her awake. When they told her about the creepy couple in the room next door, and how that room had been stretched out as long as the local playing field, their grandma tutted and shook her head.

"You ate some of that cheese didn't you?" she said, looking Joan sternly in the eyes. "I told you not to touch it, didn't I?"

Brother and sister looked at each other, shamefaced, and admitted sneaking down to the pantry to sample some of the cheese. Neither of them could be persuaded to return to their bed, so they slept with their grandmother for the remainder of that night.

The next day the two children eventually plucked up the courage to go and have a look at their bedroom. They peeked round the door, ready to run away if there was any hint of what they had encountered the night before, but they saw that the guest bedroom had returned to its normal dimensions, and there was thankfully no sign of the misshapen, ultra-lanky couple.

Nightmares are usually only experienced by the person dreaming them, but Joan and Jimmy had not only shared the same frightening sights and sounds of that bad dream, but the nightmare somehow continued into the waking world.

Later that year, Joan, Jimmy and a cousin named Martin stayed at the house on Downing Road, and on this occasion, the children once again consumed the green cheese in the pantry, despite their grandmother's orders not to do so and their salutory experience on their previous visit. This time, at four in the morning, Martin woke the other two as he yelled out in a dreadful state, shaking and trembling uncontrollably, with tears running down his face. Joan glanced groggily over at her cousin, but some movement in the corner of her eye made her glance towards the door. The wall at the far end of the bedroom was steadily receding into the distance without a sound, until it seemed as if she was looking down a long, dark tunnel.

Jimmy woke next, and sat bolt upright in bed, disorientated, trying to catch his breath, obviously waking from a nightmare. Once again, the elongated couple came waltzing crazily from the far end of the room as faint music played in the background, but upon this occasion, before the stilt-legged couple got anywhere near them, the doors of the wardrobe to the right of the room burst open, and two hideous-looking dwarves in bowler hats, with chalk-white, rosy-cheeked faces, charged at the three children gabbling a stream of nonsensical words.

The three children pelted out of that room, screaming at the tops of their voices and were chased by the diminutive, bowler-hatted dwarves across the hallway. This time, their grandmother wasn't as easily roused from her sleep as on the previous occasion, for she had enjoyed a few shots of rum – "for purely medicinal reasons," she had said, – before retiring to her bed. When she did wake up she found herself in a bed crowded with cowering grandchildren.

After having listened to their seemingly far-fetched accounts, she tried to reassure them by saying they'd had nothing but a nightmare, induced no doubt by the green cheese in the pantry. Then the grandmother got the shock of her life when she saw what she initially thought was a child in a bowler hat, peeping round the door, which had been left ajar. The face of the peeking figure was certainly no child. It was repulsive and terrifying and made the hackles rise on the back of her neck. The old woman always slept with a hammer under her bed in case of burglars, and she reached for it and hurled it at the weird-looking midget, but it hit the door instead and richocheted back into the room. But it had the effect of frightening the figure, which slinked back into the hallway. The Grandmother, Joan, Jimmy and Martin did not budge from that bed until the morning sun was fully risen and shone brightly through the bedroom window. The children were so shaken up by the creepy incidents of that night, that they never stayed at their Gran's home again.

To this day, Joan has no explanation for the strange events that took place at the house on Downing Road, but she is convinced that the forbidden green cheese somehow acted as the catalyst which unleashed the bizarre and frightening goings-on there.

In September 2005, the British Cheese Board published the findings of a study they had undertaken into whether cheese could cause nightmares. The research established that: eighty-five per cent of females who ate Stilton had some of the most unusual dreams of the whole study. Sixty-five per cent of people eating Cheddar dreamt about celebrities, over sixty-five per cent of the participants eating Red Leicester revisited their schooldays. All female participants who ate British Brie enjoyed nice relaxing dreams, whereas male participants had anxiety-inducing, cryptic dreams. Two thirds of all those who ate Lancashire cheese had a dream about work and over half of Cheshire cheese eaters had a dreamless sleep.

NIGHT VISITORS

In the world of the paranormal, one of the most frightening entities is the 'incubus' – a malevolent being which manifests itself as a tangible spirit, or sometimes as a subtle force that makes itself felt in the bedroom of the haunted person. People unlucky enough to be haunted by these creatures of the night often experience the sensation of something sitting on their feet as they lie in bed, and others may feel something pressing on the mattress, as if someone solid was sitting on the bed. These are often the first signs which presage the start of what is known as the 'Night Terror' – where the sleeper awakes, paralysed, often sensing a presence in the bedroom, but unable to establish exactly what it is, or be able to do anything about it.

In extreme cases, people have awakened to the sensation of something heavy pressing on their chest, whilst others have opened their eyes to behold frightening and often grotesque shadowy beings prancing about on their bed. The most famous of these night visitors is known as the Old Hag, which I have documented in my books before, but it would seem there are a wide variety of nocturnal visitants which can plague the sleeper.

In the autumn of 2005 a man named Simon awoke at three in the morning to find a naked woman crawling all over him in his bed at his Huyton home. Her eyes were jet black, with yellow pupils, and from her thin lips came a snake-like hiss. The woman actually bit at Simon, who was so terrified that he suffered a severe asthma attack. He stumbled out of bed and managed to turn on the light.

His bed was in total disarray, the covers being flung all over the bedroom by invisible hands, but there was no sign of the woman.

After checking my files, I discovered that there were two further reports of night terror on the road in Huyton where Simon now sleeps surrounded by crucifixes and a Bible.

Also on that same road, a few years ago, a woman went up into her six-year-old daughter's room to check on her and saw what she at first thought was her little girl, sitting on the bed. Then, through the bedroom window, the woman noticed that her daughter was actually playing outside in the garden. The 'thing' which she had mistakenly taken to be her child started laughing in an adult voice.

"What's going on?" she asked. "Turn round so I can see who you are."

But the thing refused.

Sensing that she was up against something sinister and unnatural, the terrified mother ran out of the house, grabbed her daughter, and went to stay in her sister's house for two days until she could muster up enough courage to go back home. A month after that, the woman's daughter started to scream in the middle of the night, saying there was "something horrible" in her room. The haunting has now ceased in that house but a heavy uneasiness lingers in the bedrooms each night.

~

The classic night visitor of old was the legendary vampire, and, believe it or not, there have been many well-documented reports of vampiric beings at large in Europe, including the UK, and more specifically in Liverpool. Besides the so-called Lodge Lane vampire, which has been described elsewhere in my books, there have been reports of bloodsuckers such as the 'Greek Vampire' encountered in 1860s Liverpool (see *Strange Liverpool* for the full story) as well as that of a frightening cloaked entity that shattered the peace of a rainy Sunday night in 1886.

The incident took place at Whitsuntide, at an impressive but secluded house called Heatherlea which once stood off Priory Road in Anfield, surrounded by many rural acres, adjacent to Liverpool Cemetery.

Shortly before midnight, a fifteen-year-old girl named Felicia was rudely awakened from her slumbers when a thunderstorm broke directly overhead. The storm was accompanied by a howling wind which lashed the windows of Heatherlea with rain and hailstones and seemed to whistle its way into every crack and cranny in the house. Felicia fitfully turned over in her bed, and as she did so, she happened to glance at the window. For the split-second of a lightning flash, she saw the head and shoulders of a man silhouetted in the window frame. It was as if an intruder was perched on a ladder outside her bedroom window, looking in.

Another tremendous crash of thunder shook the house to its foundations, and simultaneously the window of Felicia's bedroom burst open and a violent gust of wind blasted into her room, sending the curtains fluttering horizontally. A shape too fast for the girl's eyes to follow, flitted into the room on the wind, and a heartbeat later Felicia saw a mysterious figure standing at the foot of the bed. He was about six feet in height with long black hair and a pale face which peeped over an arm lifting a cape. His eyes had a wildness about them and were rimmed with black circles. Felicia was struck dumb with terror and pulled her bedclothes up to her chin for protection.

The man in black slowly lowered his arm to reveal a hideous sight that would haunt the girl in flashbacks for years to come. A velvety black snake, with white eyes, uncoiled itself from around the man's neck and slithered sinuously on to the bed. All Felicia could do was close her eyes and pray that the whole thing was a nightmare, but then she felt something cold and wet tickling her cheek – the snake's quivering tongue was exploring her face. She held her breath as the serpent visited first her lips, then her nostrils and finally her eyes with its endlessly probing tongue. She felt herself go dizzy and faint and then everything went black.

When she came to, Felicia instinctively turned towards the window. The milky predawn sky could be seen through the curtains, now gently fluttering in the breeze which was blowing through the open window. She glanced at the clock. It was now half-past four in the morning, and the girl stumbled out of bed and ran non-stop to her parents' bedroom to relate the unbelievable details of the supernatural attack.

In the cold light of morning, Felicia's mother noticed two deep scarlet puncture marks below her daughter's jaw-line She immediately summoned the family physician but he was at a loss to explain their origin.

Some weeks later, Felicia and her aunt were on their way to see a show at the New Star Music Hall (nowadays known as the Playhouse Theatre), in Williamson Square, when a familiar-looking young man in a top hat and cape called out to the teenager. Felicia recognised him immediately as the weird stranger who had appeared in her bedroom with the loathsome snake on that stormy night. She choked back a scream and immediately became unsteady on her feet. Having witnessed the meeting, and noticed the effect it had on the young lady, a Mr Yarberry, proprietor of the nearby cocoa rooms, chased the fellow, but he proved to be too agile to catch. Was he merely some unknown admirer of Felicia's who had stalked her and then taken advantage of the thunderstorm and her open window to find his way into her bedroom? Or was he something much more sinister; a vampire perhaps?

~

A reader named Paul recently wrote to me to tell of an incident which took place in 1985, when he was eight years old and living at Number 18D, St Andrew's tenements – also known as the Bullring – just off Brownlow Hill.

One night he and his older cousins, Dean and Ian, were up late, watching television and eating sweets. They finally got into bed, and were ready to fall asleep, when a gust of wind came from nowhere and blew open a window in the bedroom, which spooked the three lads, giving them a nasty start. Seconds later, the door burst open, and the three boys witnessed the sudden appearance of a tall stranger wearing an eye patch and dressed in an army uniform.

Wide-eyed with disbelief, they each took in the details of the uninvited guest. In his hand he held a leash, at the other end of which a small, placid mongrel wagged its tail, cocked its head and looked expectantly at its master. Dean, the eldest of the children, bravely left the bed and ran to switch on the bedroom light, and as he did so, the military-looking man seemed to evaporate, along with his spectral dog.

The same ghost is said to have been seen by other people in the tenements, but whose apparition it is, has yet to be established.

SWAN SONG SYNDROME

There is a strange and intriguing phenomenon frequently reported to me by readers, which I call 'Swan Song Syndrome'. This occurs when a person's behaviour seems to undergo a major change, and he or she will apparently prepare for their impending death. To illustrate this I will relate the following chilling examples.

In the summer of 1986, a bouncer named Tony was in the Penny Lane Records store on Bold Street, browsing through the shelves for a cassette tape, when he suddenly stopped what he was doing and began gazing out of the window with an expressionless face, apparently having fallen into some kind of trance. The bouncer's younger brother, Alan, asked him what was wrong, and Tony mumbled that nothing was wrong, but still seemed very distant. He eventually turned away from the window and walked out of the shop without buying anything, with Alan closely in tow.

Without saying a word to his brother, Tony made his way to a local solicitor's office and told the receptionist that he'd like to make a will. Alan was flabbergasted by this and asked him why on earth he had suddenly decided to have a will drafted – he hadn't discussed it before. Why now? Tony made no response, other than to repeat his request to the receptionist, who told him to take a seat while she tried to arrange the matter for him. The will was duly drawn up, after which the bouncer set off for home with his mystified brother still in tow.

When they arrived home Tony was still behaving out of character. He sat down by the telephone and started going through the pages of his little black book, which contained the names and telephone numbers of his various friends and relations. Tony's first call was to another bouncer named John, a former friend with whom he had had a bitter quarrel three years previously. They hadn't spoken since. Alan stood, dumbstruck, as Tony patched up his longstanding differences with John, and talked of burying the hatchet – life was too short and all that. Tony then made three more similar phone calls, each of them with ex-friends whom he'd held grudges against for years. After he had finished the calls he slumped into an armchair and breathed a deep sigh of relief. He obviously felt much better for having "put his affairs in order", as he put it, but offered his mystified brother no explanation for his strange behaviour.

Imagine his brother's shock, then when, three days later, Tony died of natural causes in his sleep at his Norris Green home, at the age of just forty-one. He had not been suffering from any illness that his family and friends had been aware of and his death came as a bolt from the blue for them all.

Looking back, Alan is convinced that his brother somehow received a premonition of his death whilst in that record shop, and accordingly made plans to patch up any differences with friends he'd fallen out with and to make a will before it was too late.

~

The strangest Swan Song incident that I am aware of concerned two friends – Ernie Holt and Frank Sedgwick – in 1960s Liverpool. Both men were working at a building site in the city centre at the time of these two eerie incidents, and frequently drank in the Rising Sun pub on Tithebarn Street.

One day, at lunchtime, Frank Sedgwick was standing at the bar, talking to Ernie Holt, when he happened to glance out of the window into the deserted, rain-lashed street outside. What he saw through that window was a most bizarre spectacle, which made him feel most peculiar. A black dog was hurrying along the pavement on the other side of the road – its paws going ten to the dozen – but what was unusual was that the dog was walking backwards in a perfectly straight line! Ernie spilt some of his beer as he tried to take in what he was seeing and he attempted to attract the attention of his friend, but by the time Frank looked out of the pub window, the dog had vanished.

"It was walking backwards ... in a dead straight line. I've never seen anything like it," Ernie spluttered, wiping the spilt beer off his trousers and scanning the street through the rain flecked window.

"I think you've had too much double diamond there, mate," remarked a woman sitting in the corner, eyeing Ernie with a smirk.

Frustrated, the builder shook his head.

"Don't be so daft, I'm not drunk, I've only had half a pint, for goodness sake. That was the queerest thing I've ever seen, and I didn't like it one bit."

Ernie continued to scan the street, hoping to catch sight of the canine walking in reverse again, so that he could prove its existence to Frank and the woman in the bar. It had looked just like a film being shown backwards – except it was happening in real life.

The incident apparently had a profound effect on Ernie Holt, and that night, despite the inclement weather, he journeyed miles across the water to see his estranged wife Betty over in Rock Ferry. He had a real heart-to-heart talk with Betty about the failure of their marriage and uncharacteristically claimed that the break-up had all been his fault. He then handed her a wad of money and told her to look after their son. Betty was quite overcome and asked if he had finally made up his mind to go and live in Australia, as he had talked about living down under for years, ever since they had separated, in fact. She got the shock of her life when Ernie told her that, on the contrary, he was going nowhere. The fact was, he didn't have long to live. She thought he must have been diagnosed with some fatal disease, but Ernie shook his head, saying only that he had a terrible feeling that his time was near, and that he would soon be dead. He had never been more sure of anything in his life. The feeling had haunted him since he had seen the black dog walking backwards down Tithebarn Street on that rainy afternoon. Rationally, he couldn't really see the connection between the incident and the way that he was feeling, but he was nevertheless totally convinced that the dog had been some sinister omen of approaching death.

Betty thought he was having some sort of nervous breakdown and didn't think for a minute that what he had foreseen would actually come to pass, but, sure enough, later that week, after a night of heavy drinking, Ernie choked on his own vomit as he lay in his bed, and was found by his landlady the next morning – stone cold dead!

A month later, Frank Sedgwick was walking up Tithebarn Street with another fellow worker from the building site named Ronnie Hughes. As the men entered the Rising Sun pub, Ronnie heard a clicking sound behind him, and upon turning round to see what it was, he too saw the black Newfoundland dog hurrying past – in reverse. Ronnie did a double take then walked out of the pub hallway and watched the dog disappear backwards around the corner. He shook his head and smiled. Frank asked him what he was looking at.

"I think we might be on Candid Camera, mate."

"What do you mean?" Frank asked.

"Some dog's just walked past here, and it was going backwards in a straight line," Ronnie told him, expecting his friend to burst out laughing.

But Frank's jaw dropped. He said nothing at first, but later, when the drink had loosened his tongue, he told Ronnie Hughes about the black dog which the late Ernie Holt had seen four weeks back, and how he had interpreted it as an omen of death.

"Thanks for cheering me up, mate."

The story played on Ronnie Hughes' mind all that evening, and after downing six pints, he despondently made his way home. Convinced he was going to die, he rushed into his wife's arms and told her that he loved her, even though he had never been one to openly show his feelings towards her.

Gradually, over the next fortnight the feeling that he was about to die subsided and Ronnie began to breathe more easily. Then, one day at work Ronnie was operating a pneumatic machine that was used to pump concrete into the footings on the building site, when the machine suddenly juddered to a halt. He pulled up the wide feeder tube and saw that it was blocked by a cluster of pebbles, so he pressed a certain button on the panel to blow the pebbles out of the tube, but instead an air blockage in the pneumatic compressor caused the cement and pebbles to blow backwards out of the tube with the force of a shotgun. The pebbles blasted Ronnie in the abdomen and stomach, violently hurling his body thirty feet across the building site.

Frank Sedgwick heard the loud bang and rushed to the scene of the accident. A sickening sight awaited him. Ronnie's intestines had spilled out of the appalling wound in his abdomen and it was obvious that he was going to die. Ronnie struggled to say something to Frank, but his efforts were made unintelligible by the blood which gurgled in his throat. An ambulance was upon the scene within minutes, but Ronnie was dead upon arrival at the Royal Hospital.

When Frank returned to the building site, later that evening to collect his belongings, he noticed a black dog gazing at him through the wire fence, and his blood ran cold. Fearing the dog was the very same one that the two deceased men had seen before their deaths, he quickly turned away and walked off the site. Losing your job was one thing, losing your life was another.

BOXING BULLY

In the blazing summer of 1939, a gang of five boys, all aged twelve, were happily playing football in Wavertree Park, when the local bully, a burly thirteen-year-old wearing a green and black striped shirt, came running out of the park's wooded area towards the boys. All the children who lived in the area were intimidated by Patrick Mullens, whose name brought fear to their hearts, and when the boys saw him approach, two of them quickly sneaked away, such was the tyrant's formidable reputation.

The previous year, Mullens had perpetrated a reign of terror on an innocent boy from one of the local schools, culminating in a lethal game of cat and mouse. So frightened was his lad, and so determined was he to escape Mullen's clutches, that he had run blindly into the road and been knocked down and killed by a passing car.

Upon this infernal August afternoon, Mullens closed in on Michael Sullivan, who was one year his junior.

"Give me them," said Mullens, snatching the paper bag of mint balls out of Sullivan's hand. "Mmm. My favourites. Ta very much."

He then turned his attentions to a small, slim child nicknamed Tiny Thompson and he grabbed the football out of his hand.

"Give me that back, Paddy," said Tiny, meekly, but Mullens turned around and slapped the slightly built boy hard in the face, catching his nose and making it bleed.

As Tiny cried and held his bleeding nose, Mullens sampled another of the purloined mintballs, and spun the football on one finger, then stared at Michael Sullivan with a mock quizzical expression.

"You look like a flippin' girl," he said. "Are you one?"

Sullivan, clenched his fists, and inwardly seethed. He hated Mullens but didn't dare oppose him. Mullens walked towards him with an insane look in his eyes, and Sullivan's heart pounded with fear.

All of a sudden, an old man appeared upon the scene and intervened between victim and bully.

"Now, now, boys. This is no way to settle an argument," he said, keeping them at arm's length.

He then turned to Mullens and challenged him to settle any issues he had with Sullivan in a boxing ring, under the supervision of a proper referee, with the fight fought fairly and squarely according to the Queensberry Rules.

"Unless, of course, you're scared, that is," he added.

Mullens visibly squirmed – his authority had never been challenged before, let alone by an old busybody – and he knew that he couldn't afford to lose face in front of the younger boys, so he tried to bluff his way out of the situation.

"Scared? Me?" he said with a false laugh. "I'm not scared of anybody – in or out of the boxing ring – and I'm definitely not scared of that little pip squeak Sullivan."

"Fine! So be it," said the old man and he said that he would arrange to have a boxing ring put up in the park for the following Sunday at three o'clock.

At first, Mullens tried to wriggle out of the challenge, but two girls strolling through the park came within earshot and asked what was going on. The bully couldn't resist trying to impress them and told them about the contest scheduled for the following Sunday and he bragged about how he was going to knock out "That yellow squirt Sullivan into the middle of next week".

Michael Sullivan was utterly petrified by the prospect of a fight with the thickset Mullens. There were no two ways about it, he'd end up battered to a pulp. His brain started working overtime, considering all the options. He toyed with the idea of going into hiding, or even leaving home. The old man realised how frightened he was by the expression on his face and so he accompanied the boy home and had a talk with his father, Joe Sullivan. He told him about the incident with Mullens in the park and about the proposed boxing match next Sunday.

Joe Sullivan was incensed at the idea at first and flatly refused to give his permission. He knew Mullens only too well and felt that his son was bound to lose, and lose badly. He could get seriously injured and he wasn't prepared to take that risk. However, the old man persisted. He argued that the best way to deal with bullies was to meet them head on and and the best way to do that would be to let the two youngsters settle their differences in the boxing ring, fairly and squarely.

"Fair or not, Michael would still lose. Have you seen the size of that Mullens?"

"You're right. In normal circumstances Michael wouldn't stand a chance, but I've got a cunning trick up my sleeve that will ensure victory for young Michael."

His secret weapon would be hypnotism. The old man said that, under hynosis, he could transform Michael into a fearless opponent, which would give him a sizeable advantage over Mullens. Albeit with grave misgivings, Joe Sullivan finally agreed to the boxing match. He realised that something drastic had to be done about Mullens – his reign of terror had gone on long enough – and this might just be what was called for.

Mr Hackett, the park keeper, turned a blind eye to the boxing event, which took place as planned on the following Sunday. Word had got round about the fight and crowds of people were in attendance. Before the fight, the old man hypnotised Michael Sullivan and removed all fear from his mind. The boy then launched a vicious, yet co-ordinated, attack on Mullens, and knocked him to the ground twice in the second round. Sullivan eventually won on points, and the bully Mullens was utterly humiliated in front of half the neighbourhood. How would this look on his patch? A little upstart like Sullivan beating him in the boxing ring. Not only was his pride hurt, but he had sustained a multitude of cuts and bruises during the fight and so superior had Sullivan been in the ring that, from that time onward, Mullens lived in mortal fear of the lad he had once persecuted.

The identity of the old man who hypnotised Michael Sullivan is unknown, but there were rumours that he had once been a renowned boxing coach who had worked with legendary Liverpool pugilist Jem Mace, who is buried in Anfield Cemetery.

Hypnotherapy is occasionally used in sport nowadays to help sportsmen and women achieve the right mental attitude, but it was first used in Liverpool in 1939, in an ad hoc boxing match which was staged to teach a bully a lesson he'd never forget.

ARROWS IN THE SNOW

One blazing hot day in July 1815, the sailing ship *Lothair* glided into the Liverpool Docks having just crossed the Atlantic from North America. Amongst the gaggle of excited passengers who disembarked from the vessel that day was a rich Scottish merchant named John Allan, accompanied by his wife Frances, her younger sister Nancy, and the couple's rather sickly-looking six-year-old adopted son, Edgar.

The Allans were greeted on the dockside by Thomas MacKenzie – a cousin of William Mackenzie, the Scottish railway engineer entombed in the famous pyramidal tomb on Rodney Street. Thomas MacKenzie had secured the services of two trustworthy and hardworking Liverpool maidservants – Isabel Cook and Joan Slaidburn – to accompany the Allan family on their forward journey to Irvine in Scotland. Isabel's seven-year-old sister Mary joined the party and became a playmate for little Edgar, the Allans' adopted son, when they arrived in Scotland.

Just a week before Christmas, little Mary took it upon herself to go out into the nearby woods one snowy afternoon to collect holly and ivy with which to decorate the Allans' home. Young Edgar accompanied the Liverpool girl, and somehow managed to slip out of the cottage unnoticed – his parents tended to wrap the child in cottonwool and he would never have been allowed out in such inclement weather if they had known about Mary's plan.

The two children gambolled about in the snow like two puppies. It was such a relief to be out of doors in the fresh highland air. Edgar, in particular, was invariably cooped up inside the house and he envied the local children who had the freedom of the countryside. They had soon collected whole bunches of holly laden with berries and fruiting ivy and placed them in Mary's basket along with mountains of pine cones. Wouldn't everyone be pleased when they took them back home? There would be enough to decorate the whole house. They had just agreed that it was about time that they returned home, when a strange incident occurred.

An invisible hand – or foot – was mysteriously drawing a trail of arrows in the snow which lay thick and virginal on the ground. The two children looked on in astonishment as one arrow after another was traced in the snow. They followed the arrows, and at one point, Mary wrote "Who are you?" in the snow with the tip of her umbrella – and the invisible doodler sharply crossed out the question with three lines. This gave the children a start and made them feel uneasy, but their curiosity was even stronger than their fear and so they followed the arrows which continued to appear, one after the other, snaking through the wood until eventually they led to a small lake where the children had been forbidden to go.

Suddenly, Edgar realised that he and Mary had been lured on to the thin ice at the edge of the frozen lake. The ice creaked and groaned ominously, ready to give way, and Edgar just managed to seize Mary by the arm and drag her to safety in the nick of time. The children then heard the voice of an old woman cursing them from somewhere amongst the snow-laden branches of the trees which encircled the lake. They peered into the trees but could see no one, so they ran home as fast as their legs would carry them and told the adults what had happened. They both received a good telling off and were sent to bed without any supper, but it was obvious to the adults that something untoward had happened in the wood that afternoon, and Mary's seventeen-year-old sister Isabel set off to investigate the arrows, expecting to find some kind of animal tracks, probably those of a large bird.

However, almost as soon as she arrived in the wood she found the arrows – they really did exist after all – and she traced them, and the children's footsteps, through the trees and to the lake's edge. She was horrified to see that their footsteps actually went out on to the icy surface of the lake and she realised that they had had a very lucky escape. They could both so easily have fallen through the ice and drowned.

She was just about to retrace her steps back through the wood when she recoiled in horror – for there, barely visible under the thin icy surface of the lake, floated the lifeless face of a child – and the sight of it sent the servant screaming for help.

Police later discovered that the body of the unfortunate child trapped under the ice was that of six-year-old Carol McClean, a farmer's daughter who had been reported missing some days before. John Allan was of the opinion that the arrows had been drawn in the snow as a deliberate lure for the local children – a lure that would lead them to almost certain death. He was also convinced that they had been put there by the evil spirit of a witch known as Old Nelly.

Apparently, Old Nelly had been deliberately drowned in the lake by the local villagers over a hundred years ago, as a punishment for her witchcraft, which they felt was damaging their crops and bringing death and disease to themselves and their animals. A total of nine children had drowned in the lake since that time, most probably lured to their deaths by Old Nelly's evil sorcery. Mary Cook and Edgar Allan were therefore even more fervently warned to stay well away from that lake, and this time they needed no persuading.

Incidentally, Edgar Allan later grew up to become Edgar Allan Poe, the most famous horror-story writer of all time. Perhaps this early brush with the supernatural acted as a catalyst for his brilliant and fertile imagination.

BACK YARD PICNIC

At five o'clock on the Monday morning of 19 January 1931, nine tons of solid gold passed through the city of Liverpool. The precious cargo – worth over a hundred million pounds by today's standards – was transported from the hold of a Spanish ship berthed at the Canada Dock, before being rushed through the streets in a fleet of armour-plated lorries, protected by armed guards. The gold bullion, shipped in from Madrid, was taken to a specially modified train waiting at Lime Street station, destined to strengthen the coffers of the Bank of England and other temples of Mammon in London.

As the unimaginable fortune trundled through the deserted winter thoroughfares, it passed by many a family living the most marginal of existences in dreadful housing conditions. In one such draughty, dilapidated house off Great Homer Street, four dreamy little heads slept soundly on their pillows, untroubled by their circumstances – they had never known any better. Just the tiniest fraction of that nine tons of wealth would have brought a dramatic change to the quality of those children's lives in Depression-hit Liverpool.

Three boys, George, aged ten, the twins, Alan and Sam, aged seven, and their six-year-old sister Lily, awoke, side by side like peas in a pod in their bed that morning, and after a breakfast of porridge prepared by their fifty-six-year-old Aunt Cynthia, they were told the good news. The pipes at their school had burst because of the intense cold and the place had been flooded.

"So, no school today," Cynthia told the orphaned children.

"Hurray!" they chorused, smiling and rubbing their hands with glee.

Cynthia smiled too but her smile barely disguised the anxiety which these days seemed to be permanently etched on her face. What hard times they were living through – life had become one long unending struggle. Her sister's children entrusted into her care huddled around the lambent blue flames of the gas fire as their aunt wondered how she could possibly continue to make ends meet and keep on feeding their hungry mouths. Recently she had been reduced to cadging damaged cakes from the Sayers shop round the corner to satisfy their growing appetites, and kind Mr Lucas the baker often offered her an extra loaf, free of charge, as Cynthia had once nursed his wife back to health after a long illness.

Now, on this freezing Monday morning, the widowed Cynthia had another problem to deal with – how to keep her boisterous nephews and niece occupied while the school remained closed. She made her living as a charwoman, and was due to clean a house at 10 o'clock, so she told the eldest nephew, George, that she'd be gone for just over an hour, and that he was to look after the little ones and not let anyone into the house in her absence. She closed the front door feeling decidedly uneasy. She knew the children were really too young to be left by themselves, but what choice did she have?

As she scrubbed, cleaned and dusted she thought of nothing else but the four children alone in the house by themselves. What if there was a fire, or an accident? What if they opened the door to a stranger? The hour seemed to drag by so slowly but eventually it was over and she was able to rush home and check up on the children. As she opened the door her worst fears were realised – the children were no longer there. She searched each of the damp, sparsely-furnished rooms, and even checked down the coal cellar, but she could find no trace of them. Then she noticed a note on the sideboard, written in George's distinct childish scrawl, which read, 'Gone for a picnic'. The note gave her no comfort. She never allowed the children to go further than the end of the street by themselves, and besides, it was a freezing cold January day. Where on earth could George have taken them for this picnic?

The police were informed, and the local streets and parks were searched. Sunlight finally broke through the overcast skies, but did little to brighten the prospect of locating the missing children. Cynthia's religious neighbour, Mrs McCarthy, lit four candles for the children at the local church and said some prayers for their safe return. She then comforted Cynthia at her humble home, and assured her that the children would soon be found safe and well – they were good kids, surely they couldn't have gone far.

At half-past one, Cynthia and her friend heard a familiar sound – it was little Lily laughing, and it was coming from the back yard. What sweet music that child's laughter was to the women's ears.

"How stupid!" said Cynthia. "I never thought to look in the back yard. Come on, let's go and see if they're there."

The two women rushed into the kitchen and pulled the net curtains away from the window. What they saw was one of the sweetest sights they could imagine. The children, all muffled up in their hat, coats and scarves, were having a picnic in the tiny back yard. They had laid a chequered tablecloth down on the flagstones and were sitting on it. They'd also brought a jug of milk, some bread, a jar of jam, and even a bowl of wax fruit out into the yard – "To make it look more like a proper picnic" they explained. Cynthia and her neighbour ran outside and smothered the four children with kisses and then informed the police that they had been found.

After a while, Mrs McCarthy brought out a newly-set jelly from her house next door as her contribution to the unusual picnic, and Aunt Cynthia treated the children to sarsapirilla and apple pie. The two women sat in their heavy coats alongside the children as the precious January sunshine filtered through the smoking chimney pots into the back yard. They all seemed to be enjoying the brick wall scenery as if they were savouring the breathtaking vistas of Tuscany's rolling hills.

That evening, before the children went to bed, they intrigued their aunt by telling her about a woman in a long dress and white apron who had served them pieces of "a pink fish" which tasted delicious. The children all agreed on the woman's description. She had brown hair tied up in a bun, and had a smiling, rosy-cheeked face. She'd appeared out of nowhere and said nothing to them, and after giving the children the fish – which Cynthia thought was probably salmon – she had gone into the kitchen.

Cynthia thought this all sounded a little spooky, and the next day she asked Mrs McCarthy, what she thought about the story of the brown-haired woman in the apron. Mrs McCarthy said that she sounded like a ghost, and the two women decided to consult eighty-three-year-old Mrs Mills, the oldest person living in the street, who was a mine of information about the old neighbourhood and everyone who had lived there.

What Mrs Mills told the two women made their hair stand on end. She said that around forty years back, a man had murdered his wife in the house where Cynthia now lived. Apparently, the husband, a fishmonger, gradually lost his mind and one Sunday night, in an insane frenzy, he hacked off his wife's head in the bedroom and threw her severed head down the stairs. Not surprisingly, soon after the savage crime was discovered the murderer was committed to a mental hospital, where he would spend the remainder of his life. His wife's death was particularly tragic because she had been a very kind and generous woman, who often treated the starving, barefoot children of the neighbourhood to helpings of fish and bread, and she was greatly missed by them all.

Years after the murder, different people who had moved into the house had seen and heard the severed head clattering down the stairs. Cynthia shivered when she heard this, because she remembered what the children had said about the pink fish which the woman had given them, and she also recalled that on some evenings – usually Sunday evenings now she came to think of it – she had heard the sounds of something thudding down the stairs ...

In the following year, Cynthia's fortunes changed dramatically for the better when she met a wealthy businessman who fell in love with her. Not only that, it turned out that he loved children and he took Cynthia and her nephews and niece under his wing. Then, at the age of fifty-seven, the widow married for the second time, and was only too delighted to say goodbye to the haunted house off Great Homer Street.

A Life that Could Have Been

In the summer of 1909, the fortunes of the Holland family of Nottingham took a severe turn for the worse. They descended overnight from a life of ease and opulence into a grim existence of extreme hardship. Charles Holland had lost most of his personal fortune in a disastrous business venture. Then his wife had died during the early months of her pregnancy from a fever, leaving him feeling utterly bereft.

One night, faced with being an outcast from high society, and emotionally torn apart by the loss of his beloved wife, Elizabeth, Charles had decided that he could no longer carry on. Shutting himself inside his study he removed a pistol from his desk drawer and placed the barrel into his mouth. His hand trembled on the trigger as wave after wave of hopelessness and despair swept over him, but he was stopped at the last moment from ending his life because of his beloved twelve-year-old son Ambrose. The child walked into his father's study that fateful afternoon, just seconds before Charles was due to pull the trigger.

"Papa! Papa! What are you doing?" cried the child.

Charles Holland met his gaze and slowly let the pistol fall into his lap.

"Nothing, Ambrose. Papa was just fooling about," he sighed, his head drooping on his chest. "That is all."

In that moment he knew that he couldn't carry out his plan. He just couldn't do that to his beloved son, whom he drew to himself and squeezed tightly, as his body was wracked with great, gulping sobs. Afterwards he felt strengthened by this outpouring of emotion and somehow managed to pull himself together. He realised that, for the sake of his son who had already lost his mother, he had no other choice than to face up to the rough road that lay ahead, and he quietly slipped the pistol back into the drawer.

Within days, the bailiffs called and removed everything of value from the house, and Charles was forced to move in with a less fortunate cousin who lived in a small terraced house on Sutton Street, near Liverpool's Newsham Park. Young Ambrose had been accustomed to a life of luxury, and found the streets of his new neighbourhood grim and unfriendly – he stood out from the other children because of his fine clothes and educated accent – he just didn't fit in.

One summer morning, Ambrose, resplendent in his top hat and Sunday best clothes, packed his case as instructed by his father, and waited at a tramstop. He was to visit a female relative in Low Hill, in the hope of staying with her for a week while his father recovered from influenza. Whilst waiting for the tram, three working-class boys aged about eleven or twelve, gathered round Ambrose, making fun of him and calling him a 'snooty snob'. A minor scuffle ensued and one of the boys knocked off Ambrose's topper. The three lads ran off gleefully throwing the hat to one another, but Ambrose couldn't give chase as his tram had just arrived.

A week later, Ambrose returned home, and his father told his only son that he had found him a school to attend locally. Ambrose started at the school the next day, but his heart sank when he saw that the three boys who had fought with him at the tramstop attended the very same school. Initially, egged on by the three boys, the other children bullied Ambrose because of his well-spoken accent and gentlemanly manners, but although he was derided for belonging to another class, he was a very kind and friendly child who showed great skill at football and this soon earned him the respect of his fellow pupils. The three boys who had battled with him, Bobby, Johnny and Jim, soon became close friends, and they often played football together on the huge recreation ground adjacent to Lister Drive. When a couple of roughs from Fairfield tried to victimise Ambrose because of the way he spoke and dressed, Bobby and Johnny came to blows with them and sent them packing.

Ambrose was fascinated by the disadvantaged lives his new-found friends lived, and he developed a great sympathy for the poor. In Nottingham, Ambrose had had very few companions of his own age, as he had spent most of his time closeted away with his governess. He felt himself very fortunate to have friends as close as Bobby, Johnny and Jim, and he was acutely aware of the fact that, although his companions were virtually penniless, they always shared their sweets with him.

Love also blossomed for Ambrose that eventful year. He noticed a pretty girl of about thirteen who used to stand shyly watching the impromptu football matches each day. Weeks went by before Ambrose plucked up the courage to kiss Nelly Hughes, but after that they were soon holding hands and taking long walks together in Newsham Park, making earnest promises of undying love.

It then happened that Ambrose's father had a lucky break when a friend rescued him from bankruptcy and penury with an offer of a major position with a company in London. A grateful Charles Holland uprooted himself once more and took his son to live in Mayfair. Ambrose was very sorry to have to leave his three good friends and was heartbroken to be parted from his sweetheart, Nelly. He wrote to her regularly from his new London home but he never received any replies.

Apparently, at the age of sixteen, after repeatedly pleading with his father, Ambrose revisited Liverpool to look for Nelly and his three chums. He was crestfallen when he found that Nelly was already married and living in poverty with two hungry children. The two looked looked deep into each other's eyes, their expressions full of regret and the recognition that, if their lives had not been forced along different paths, they would have still been together. To his dismay, Ambrose also discovered that two of his close friends had turned to crime – like so many other young men who are trapped in a cycle of poverty – and were serving time in prison.

Most tragic of all, Ambrose was to perish just days after his eighteenth birthday, whilst fighting for his country in the Great War in the stinking trenches in Northern France.

Nelly never forgot her first love, and at the very moment when Ambrose was killed on the Western Front, she saw a vision of his terrible death in the coals of the fire round which she had been huddling at her Kensington home. The girl passed out as she watched the ghostly scenes of trench warfare played out in the flames, and the body of her sweet, gentle Ambrose being torn apart by flying shrapnel, then left to rot in the filthy, stagnant mud of the trench.

THE PILLBOX GHOST

Just before noon on Saturday 24 September 1955, eleven-year-old Peter Williams, a pupil at Grange Secondary School, left his parents' home at Walby Close on the Woodchurch Estate, Birkenhead, and set off to pick blackberries with some friends. Accompanying Peter were eleven-year-old Brian Lennon, his four-year-old brother Alec, and twelve-year-old John Williams, all of whom lived on nearby New Hey Road.

The children headed for a railway embankment on the north side of the Woodchurch Estate to start their blackberry-picking. It did not take them long to fill the assorted containers which Peter's mother had given them. Whilst the other three youngsters were sitting eating some of the blackberries, Peter Williams idly decided to explore inside an old concrete pillbox-like structure – originally used by the Home Guard in wartime. He soon came across what he at first thought was a shop-window dummy lying sprawled on the concrete floor. However, when he took a closer look, he realised to his horror that he was looking at the body of a woman with a pile of clothes heaped on top of her face. The boy quickly alerted his friends who each, in turn, braced themselves and took a look at the body. Then, in a highly distressed state, Peter raced home to tell his mother about the gruesome find and thus began the baffling Pillbox Murder case.

Within a short time of the discovery of the body, CID officers, headed by the Deputy Chief Constable, Superintendent Tankard, were at the scene of the crime. A cadre of uniformed policemen arrived at the railway embankment soon afterwards and formed a tight cordon around the pillbox to keep back the crowds of voyeuristic sightseers who had gathered to catch a glimpse of the murdered woman's corpse. It was established that the unidentified woman, who looked between fifty and sixty years of age, had been strangled and then mutilated. The cryptic three-word sentence 'I am VD' had been scrawled on her body in red lipstick.

The Police immediately launched a full-scale murder investigation, ultimately amassing over a thousand statements from witnesses, and even bringing in a top Scotland Yard detective to co-ordinate the enquiry. Early clues looked quite promising. A Birkenhead Corporation woodsman at Arrowe Park, Leslie Poole, told police how, on the morning after the murder, at precisely 8.10am, he had found a trail of footprints in the dew-drenched grass, leading out of a wood close to the pillbox. William Shaw, another member of the park ground-staff, said that, at 6pm, two days before the discovery of the body, he had seen a couple sitting in a shelter by the local bowling greens, and heard the woman say, "I am much older than you are."

Nevertheless, as the days wore on, even the identity of the murder victim remained a mystery, until the police controversially decided to put the face of the dead woman in the *Liverpool Echo* – and then came the first breakthrough. Several readers of the *Echo* instantly recognised the dead woman as Alice Barton. A copy of the *Echo* found its way into the hands of John Barton, the fifty-six-year-old husband of the murdered woman, and shocked him to his marrow, for he had not set eyes upon his wife since she had walked out on him during the Christmas holiday of 1943.

Police took Mr Barton from his home in Hindley Green to Price Street Mortuary, Birkenhead, where he made a positive identification of his wife's mortal remains. Scotland Yard and Birkenhead CID then learnt that Alice Barton had been staying at St Winifred's Hotel – situated at the junction of Knowsley Road and Rimrose Road in Bootle – in the days before her murder, but why, and how she was able to afford to stay at the hotel, despite having no known employment, remained – like the Pillbox Murder itself – an enduring mystery.

In March 1957, the first sighting of what seems to have been Alice Barton's earthbound ghost was seen near the Woodchurch estate, about two hundred yards away from the pillbox where the murder had taken place. A postman spotted the figure of a woman, apparently gliding along as if it was on wheels, moving towards the pillbox structure. The apparition was ethereal and indistinct, but unmistakably that of a woman.

When word got out of this ghost sighting, there were other reports of people seeing a phantom woman, and in the summer of 1957, five adults from Birkenhead foolishly congregated in the pillbox with an upturned glass and a ouija board, in an attempt to contact the spirit of Mrs Barton in the hope of obtaining information about her killer. After twenty minutes of garbled messages, the name of a male came through (a name which I cannot divulge for legal reasons) at which point the glass flew violently off the board and smashed into the wall of the pillbox with such velocity, that a shard of glass embedded itself in the cheek of one of the sitters. The name spelt out by the ouija board was being carefully copied down by torchlight, when a terrifying incident took place.

One of the shadows cast by the women in the pillbox suddenly started to dance about, although the woman herself remained motionless. The group quickly realised that the silhouette was not that of the woman sitting round the ouija board, but was of a ghost – probably the murdered woman's! The shadow had initially looked flat and two-dimensional, like a normal shadow – until it moved, that is – and then they quickly realised that it was actually supernatural.

Within seconds, the concrete walls of the pillbox reverberated with the screams of a woman in dire distress, which shattered the tense silence. The amateur spiritualists nearly jumped out of their skins in terror, and the upturned ouija board and glass clattered to the concrete floor as they scrambled out of the pillbox and ran away from the murder scene as fast as their legs could carry them.

NIGHT TERRORS

There is a type of ghost which is particularly frightening because it does not haunt houses, but people. Such tormenting phantoms often manifest themselves out of the blue for no apparent reason and then haunt a person, sometimes daily, as regularly as clockwork, or alternatively intermittently over the space of many years, and no matter where the person goes, the entity follows.

In 1981, a horror film called *The Entity* was released, which featured just such a person-centred haunting. The demonic entity featured in the movie actually raped a woman and victimised her repeatedly, no matter where she went. The film was based upon the well-documented case of a woman in Culver City, California, who was repeatedly raped with the utmost violence in her own home by a sinister supernatural force (interpreted as a demon) which followed her about, even after she had moved five times.

Closer to home, here in Liverpool, there have been similar cases reported from the Victorian era to the present day. Here is a letter from a woman who asked me not to divulge her real name:

Dear Tom,

From 1997 to the present day, my daughter and I have been persecuted by something terrifying that invades our beds after dark. I hope you will believe me and hopefully advise me on ridding my home of these evil entities. In May 1997 I was living in the Croxteth area of Liverpool with my daughter, then aged 15. I had been separated from my husband since 1994. On May 31, 1997, which I remember being a Saturday night, I went to bed around half-past twelve. My daughter had already gone to bed at 10.30pm.

Around one in the morning, I felt something sit down on the edge of my bed, near the bottom. It was so heavy I thought a burglar was sitting on the bed, and was so terrified, I just pretended I was asleep. I then felt something cold get into the bed with me and lay beside me. I knew it was something supernatural by the way it got into the bed without lifting the duvet, in such a fast way. I turned away from this thing and it somehow slid over me, like a snake almost. For a brief moment I opened my eyes, and saw the most terrifying face on my pillow, facing me. I shouted, "Go away!" but then this thing had its way with me – actually had intercourse with me.

When it left the bed I jumped up, turned on the bedroom light, ran into the hallway, switched on the light there, then did the same in the lounge, where I tried to smoke a cigarette as I cried.

This lady's letter then went on to describe how her daughter reported the same experience with what seems to have been the same entity. Mother and daughter assumed the house, which was rather old, was haunted by something truly evil and eventually moved to a more modern house in Old Swan, hoping that that would be an end to their problems.

For the first few weeks the mother and her teenaged daughter slept uneasily, fearful of the return of the chilling night visitor, but they eventually started to relax. Then, in the January of 1998, the thing – whatever it was – did return. The mother was lying in her bed with the radio tuned to Radio 2, when she realised that something was turning the volume down. The room was plunged into silence – then came a faint sniggering sound. The bed began to rock gently, and she realised with utter dread that the night terror had returned to abuse her. Its cold bony hand slid up her back, and it started to cackle. She jumped out of bed, threw back the curtains, and turned to be confronted by a hideous, misshapen, skeletal black creature of some sort with a small round head and staring black-rimmed eyes.

In a state of pure terror the victim turned on her sinister persecutor and repeatedly swore at it. The thing hissed back at her like an angry snake, then slithered off the bed into the darkness. The bedroom door, which was ajar, moved slightly, as if the thing had brushed against it on its way out, and then followed the patter of footsteps rapidly ascending the stairs – up to the room where her daughter lay sleeping. Less than a few seconds later, as the mother was fetching a large carving knife from the kitchen, she heard her daughter let out a bloodcurdling scream, followed by a succession of bumps and thumps, and the sound of demonic laughing.

The mother raced up the stairs to find her daughter coming towards her sobbing hysterically, and they both ended up barricading themselves in the living room until the break of dawn.

In desperation to be rid of their malign intruder, the mother and daughter moved once more, this time to Aigburth, but the thing turned up there as well one night, when the daughter awoke to find it crawling along on its belly towards her bed from the corner of the room.

The mother and daughter told one parapsychologist about these continual nocturnal invasions by the entity, and he advised them to seek counselling from a psychotherapist, or psychiatrist. I knew better, having read and investigated many reports of Old Hag Syndrome and succubus and incubus attacks over the many years I had spent studying this phenomenon.

The first rule about tackling these demons of the night is to try not to fear them – obviously easier said than done – but they thrive on the fear which they generate in their victims. The advice I give to those who are subjected to these attacks is that they should close their eyes if they are faced with hideous apparitions and try and shut them out. Then the God the victim believes in should be invoked to combat the entity. Even seasoned atheists will quickly call upon a higher power when they experience Old Hag, or any type of night terror visitations. Lights should always be left on, near to, or better still, in the actual room where the attacks take place, because these things that prey on people detest light – another argument which supports their possible demonic origins. Keeping a Bible in the room where the attacks take place is also a good idea, and perhaps a crucifix. As an extreme measure, the house should be blessed by a priest.

When the mother and daughter in question followed this advice, the malevolent entity finally stopped visiting them, and at the time of writing, it has failed to put in any further appearances at the mother's home. The daughter is in her early twenties now and lives close to her mother. She too has experienced nothing out the ordinary since her home was blessed, but she always sleeps with a nightlight on these days and keeps a copy of the Bible at the side of her bed – just in case!

~

In June 1911, a particularly strange and terrifying case of a person-centred haunting was reported. The body of a woman from Eccleston in Cheshire was found floating in the River Dee. Her face was contorted with an expression of intense fear, and locals were convinced that she had been the victim of the 'Straker' – a hideous demonic being whose appearance was so terrifying that its face could bring instant death to anyone who beheld it. A number of vagrants in the same area had also been found dead, and all of them wore grotesque expressions of unbridled fear, as if something had literally frightened the life out of them.

A month later, the Straker mania spread across the border to Lancashire, where the demon continued to kill various people in their homes – usually elderly men and women with weakened constitutions – by gazing in at them through windows. Several deaths attributed to the Straker were also reported in St Michael's in the Hamlet and Cressington. One man who allegedly saw the heart-stopping vision of terror peeping through his bedroom window one night managed to survive the ordeal but was rendered dumb and insane by the experience.

BAFFLING GHOSTS

Throughout Liverpool, from the humblest home to the grandest mansion, and from small corner shops to world-famous chain stores, a range of baffling ghosts abound. These are apparitions and forces that carry out eccentric routines which baffle the victim and bewilder the ghosthunter. Here are a few accounts of these perplexing entities.

~

At a certain well-known chain store on Church Street, in Liverpool city centre, a mischievous female ghost materialises from time to time and squirts water at people, usually when their backs are turned, then vanishes just as quickly.

Some people who have had the misfortune of encountering this cheeky phantom believe she dates from around the 1930s, while others think she is much older, dating back to the Edwardian or possibly the Victorian era. Why she squirts water (possibly from a siphon) is anybody's guess; she is a truly baffling ghost.

I have received numerous letters and emails from people who have encountered the spectral mischief maker, and it would be interesting to see if the closed-circuit television cameras in the store have captured her appearances (and disappearances) on tape. I will keep you posted on this one should I receive any further information.

~

In 1994, a twelve-year-old boy from Waddicar, named Stuart, went to stay at his Aunt Joan's home in the Kennesse Green area, between Maghull and Netherton. Stuart spent the weekend at his aunt's home, and on the Sunday afternoon, as

Joan was preparing a roast dinner in the kitchen, her nephew and a boy from next door decided to play hide and seek in the house as it was raining and they couldn't play out. Stuart tiptoed into his auntie's bedroom and hid in the wardrobe, then waited quietly. The boy from next door, eleven-year-old Jonathan, looked everywhere except the wardrobe, and Stuart began to get a little impatient – it was hot and stuffy inside. He opened the door a crack and peeped out – and received the shock of his life. A deranged-looking woman was sitting on Auntie Joan's bed, tugging and pulling her hair out in clumps. she seemed to be struggling to say something but was not succeeding, as if she was a mute. Stuart winced as he heard the awful sound of the woman's long locks of hair being ripped out by the roots. Her face was deathly pale, and she had dark bags beneath a pair of tormented looking eyes. She wore an outfit which Stuart later sketched for his aunt, and from the drawing it would seem that she was wearing clothes from around the 1950s.

Stuart tried to close the wardrobe door without being noticed, but the woman was on it like a flash and wrenched it open. The boy fled – passing under the woman's arm and straight out of the bedroom. The child knocked over his friend Jonathan on the landing and pelted straight down the stairs, screaming for his Aunt Joan, who almost dropped the roast beef as she took it from the oven. Joan's blood ran cold when Stuart told her about the strange woman upstairs, because her husband had repeatedly told her that he had awakened in the night to find a shadowy woman sitting on the edge of the bed. She had always taken his story with a pinch of salt but this seemed to corroborate it.

When Joan's husband came home from the pub, she sent him upstairs to see if the woman was still about, but the room was empty and the wardrobe door wide open.

From time to time the ghost still haunts the house and usually manifests itself as nothing more than a darting shape in the peripheral vision field of the witness. Guests who visit Joan's house often remark upon seeing such things out of the corner of their eyes. The identity of the ghost is still unknown, and why she pulls her hair out is anybody's guess.

~

At a house quite close to Hunt's Cross railway station, a ghost often eerily betrays its presence by leaving chessmen neatly arranged on a chessboard-topped coffee table. Mr Williams, a keen chess player, assumed that it was his nine-year-old son messing about when he first found the chess pieces laid out on the board, but soon realised that the intriguing positions in which the pawns, queens, knights, castles and bishops were left, couldn't possibly be the work of someone with no knowledge of the game.

On one occasion Mr Williams instructed his wife and other members of the family not to touch any of the pieces on the board, and over the space of three days, he actually played a very slow game of chess with his invisible opponent, with each of the pieces being moved in his absence. On the third morning Mr Williams came downstairs and thought he could actually see a pawn moving all by itself on the chessboard. Mrs Williams was unnerved by the spooky game and ordered her husband to keep the chess pieces under lock and key, thus ending any possibility of communication with the chess playing spirit. Occasionally though, when Mr Williams leaves the chess pieces out on the coffee table, he still finds them lined up on the board by an invisible hand.

I have discovered from the Williams' neighbours that, in the 1980s, an old recluse of a man used to play chess at the house – with a ghost. He had confided this strange claim to a neighbour, who had concluded that the old loner was simply going a bit senile.

~

In the late 1990s a student living in Everton told me how on some evenings when he returned to his flat, he would not only find his clothes neatly folded in piles in the bedroom, but also that some items had also been thoroughly washed, dried and ironed! He told his landlord about the strange goings-on, and was informed that in the 1950s, the flat had been used as a laundrette. Why some ghost should return from beyond the grave to wash, iron and fold a student's clothes remains yet another insoluble mystery of the supernatural.

BOZ

I have thousands of stories in my files on the paranormal, most of them unpublished, and the following tale ranks as one of the most intriguing accounts I have ever researched, related to me by a man who passed away in 2004. In the year 1913, Tommy Ellison, a twelve-year-old orphan, was sent to live with his Uncle William in Bootle after the death of his mother during childbirth. Tommy was not the brightest of lads, and had great difficulty reading and writing; he may possibly have been dyslexic – the condition had not been recognised in those days – but he had an astonishing talent for drawing and painting, and would tell anyone who asked that he wanted to be an artist when he grew up.

Tommy was lucky to have such a kind uncle and guardian as William, who looked after the boy very well at his little terraced home on Ariel Street, and treated him as if he was his own son.

One Sunday afternoon, Tommy was kicking a case-ball against the wall of the back yard when he suddenly noticed the strong aroma of something burning. He then inexplicably felt a compulsion to glance to his right, and when he did so, he saw something terrifying which left him paralysed with fear. He interpreted the thing he saw as a monster when he later described it to his uncle. A grotesque head with two large pointed ears was protruding over the wall, leaning on two arms that terminated in claw-like hands. The eyes were nothing more than dim yellow pinpricks, and although Tom was shaking, he could see from the expression on the face of this bizarre creature that it was as scared of him as he was of it.

"Uncle William!" Tom yelped, standing like a statue, unable to move, as if the nerves between his brain and his feet had suddenly been severed.

"Ssh! Be quiet, child!" said the thing, in a raspy, gravely voice, drawing a bony index finger to its large mouth.

Uncle William was busy in the parlour and didn't hear his nephew, and so never responded to his cry for help. Still rooted to the spot, Tom listened as the gargoylesque creature falteringly introduced itself as Boz, and claimed to be a repentant demon recently escaped from Hell. There was something reassuring about the way in which it nervously addressed him and as Tom was drawn in by the weird tale which the sinister entity spun, his fear of the unknown faded considerably. Boz explained that he had found a way out of Hell, where he had been incarcerated for a very long time. He said there were other demons looking for him at this very moment, and that if he was brought back to the Kingdom of Satan, he'd be severely punished and his existence would be even more miserable than it had been before.

"Then can't you ask God for help?" Tom asked innocently.

But the stone-like renegade cohort of the Devil laughed bitterly and said that he had been sentenced to eternal damnation.

"Eternal is forever," Boz sighed, and the lights of his eyes faded almost to nothing.

Boz told the boy that an angel named Shezzerael often despatched repentant demons back to Hell, and he was expecting the angel to find him any day soon.

Tom later told his Uncle William all about his meeting with the strange creature who called himself Boz, and was not believed, of course.

On several occasions after that Tommy Ellison went missing and was caught roaming the streets of Bootle in the early hours of the morning, and he tried to explain away his gallivanting by saying that he had been walking about with Boz, looking for suitable places for him to hide, as his present hiding place – somewhere in next door's back yard – was too exposed and he was certain to be discovered.

Uncle William's scepticism was lessened somewhat when his nephew told him that there was an 'opening' to Hell somewhere close, and that demons had once escaped through it and attacked a local woman, because he was aware that, in the late nineteenth century in Ariel Street, a woman named Teresa Higginson had allegedly been possessed by the Devil. It had been a well-witnessed and well-documented case that had even reached the ears of the Pope. How on earth would a twelve-year-old boy know about the case?

Uncle William became intrigued and asked his nephew about the other things which the remorseful demon had told him. Boz, it transpired, had warned Tommy that a terrible war, planned by the Devil, would soon break out on earth and would affect virtually every country in the world. World War One was indeed declared in the following year.

Uncle William began to secretly keep watch on his nephew whenever he played in the back yard. He surveyed the yard from his upstairs bedroom window, trying to determine if Boz was indeed something demonic, or simply the figment of a lonely child's imagination.

A fortnight after Boz made his first appearance to Tommy, a well-dressed man called at Uncle William's house, and claimed that he was the Reverend Canon Nickley from St Alexander's Church, and that he had been told all about Tommy Ellison's fanciful tales of the demon Boz. Tommy sensed that something was not quite right about the Reverend, especially when he asked to be shown the back yard and started poking about in every nook and cranny. After a quarter of an hour of searching, the holy man left, and Uncle William, sharing his nephew's suspicions, decided to go to the local church of St Alexander to see if there really was such a person as the Reverend Nickley. There wasn't and the priests there said they had never heard of such a man.

Tommy subsequently told his uncle that the man posing as a vicar had been none other than Shezzerael, the angel on Boz's tail.

"Right! Enough's enough!" said Uncle William, exasperated. "Let's have no more of this Boz nonsense. That fellow was probably a thief who wanted to see if we kept anything of value in the back yard. Shezzerael indeed!"

Weeks later, a terrific thunderstorm broke out in the skies over Bootle, and Tommy happened to glance out of the back window during a particularly bright lightning flash. Illuminated down below, for just the blinking of any eye, he saw a tall figure in white, which must have been almost seven feet in height, standing in the middle of the yard. It vanished before he could take in any more detail.

From that day onwards, poor Boz was never seen again, and Tom was convinced that the angel he had dreaded had finally caught up with him and sent him back to Hell.

THE DARK TALENTS OF DAVID VOTRIAN

One snowy night in the winter of 1875, a wild-eyed, foreign-looking man in his thirties arrived at Catherine Delamour's boarding house at Number 171 Duke Street. When Mrs Delamour responded to the frantic knocking on her front door, she was confronted by David Votrian who was in an agitated state. All of the beds were taken that night, but the well-spoken visitor, somehow managed to persuade a reluctant Mrs Delamour to allow him to spend the night sitting by the fireside of the communal kitchen. A gaggle of curious lodgers gathered around the latest arrival, and soon became enchanted with his strange stories of mystery and the occult.

As he roasted potatoes on the kitchen hob, Votrian revealed that he had spent seven years at a school of Black Magic in Paris, studying sorcery in a crypt that was so deep that the light of day never filtered into its murky depths. Votrian went on to tell them that his master at the school had been exiled from France by the Jesuits for resurrecting the dead, which made some of the more gullible lodgers gasp and move away from Votrian, but the more sceptical ones amongst them challenged him to give a demonstration of his alleged powers. The storyteller's eyes narrowed to slits and he reacted to their cynicism with seething rage. Shaking with fury, he uttered a jumble of unintelligible words for a while, then pointed at the fire and the coals glowing in the hob. Something moved about in those coals, and sparks jumped out of the flames.

What happened next was witnessed by Mrs Delamour, Mr Williams, the deputy of the boarding house, and many of the assembled lodgers.

A small but grotesque head with horns the colour of terracotta sprouting from its forehead, emerged from the coals, and gave the impression from its contorted expression, that it was in sheer agony. At this point, most of the lodgers fled from the kitchen in terror, but Mrs Delamour stood her ground, even though she was understandably terrified by the apparition. David Votrian, his eyes still transfixed on the fire, calmly explained that he had just, "Called up a demon from the place of damnation". Moments later, the terrifying gargoyle was gone – vanished in a puff of black smoke.

Votrian was ordered to leave the lodging house immediately, and he reluctantly concurred. The incident soon passed into local folklore – the night Mrs Delamour and her lodgers got the shock of their lives – and before long they all began to wonder if they really had seen a demon from hell in the Duke Street lodging house, or whether the enigmatic Votrian had merely played some sort of magic trick on them.

Nothing was heard of David Votrian for the next twelve years until he suddenly resurfaced from obscurity at a house on Sefton Square in the Dingle, and once more, he was soon up to his diabolical conjuring tricks. On this occasion, something sinister took place at the house of off-duty policeman John Cunningham, when a séance was held, with Votrian conducting the proceedings. Votrian was accompanied that night by John Kyffin, a local plumber, and a doctor by the name of Edmund Anderson, as well as nine other people sitting expectantly around the table.

At midnight, as a blizzard raged outside, the circle of people from many different walks of life joined hands around the circular table, and within minutes, strange, eerie forms started to materialise, hovering over a single candle in the centre of the table. One of these forms was of a bearded face which was readily recognised by one of the sitters as that of her dead uncle. At half-past midnight the candle suddenly started to splutter and spit and finally went out. Then a succession of dull thuds shook the floor.

When the candle was lit again, all the sitters bar David Votrian recoiled in terror. Standing in the middle of the room was a creature the like of which none of them had ever seen before. The figure was definitely male – in fact in most respects it was just like a man – but from its forehead sprouted two horns and its legs were animal-like, with cloven feet. Those closest to the figure claimed that it held pipes, just like those associated with the sinister old god Pan. The figure gave an unearthly laugh and then left the house, trotting across the square with a goat-like gait. Throughout, David Votrian just stared silently at the creature, his eyes like slits, whilst those around him were thrown into terror and confusion. The creature was seen by a policeman walking his beat, as it galloped away from the house, although, probably wisely, he chose not pursue it into the night.

Was this and the previous episode nothing more than some kind of elaborate practical joke, or was David Votrian a genuine, but irresponsible, dabbler in occult forces?

LIVING IN THE PAST

A retired policeman from Liverpool related the following highly unusual story to me a few years ago. In the 1990s, the decomposing body of a man in his mid-forties was discovered in the middle of a former factory on the outskirts of Liverpool. The man, who I will call Mr Smith, had been missing for some time, and his brother had informed the police about his suspicious absence. Mr Smith was a highly successful businessman and millionaire, as well as a former vice-president of a company that operated across the globe. In 1996 Mr Smith had confided in his brother that he had experienced something amazing which had affected him deeply and changed his outlook on life.

In the summer of 1996, Mr Smith had suddenly found himself overwhelmed by feelings of nostalgia and longing for his childhood, so he had taken to driving to the old neighbourhood in the Scotland Road area where he had lived as a child, and had revisited all that remained of his childhood haunts.

On one misty morning that summer he was wandering, as usual, around the old neighbourhood, experiencing all the mixed emotions that such visits invariably engender, when he suddenly found himself back in another era. At around 9.30am that morning he stopped in front of a greengrocer's with all its fruit and vegetables set out in front of the shop like they used to do when he was a child. How come he had not noticed the shop before? He quickly realised that there had been no such shop at that location the week before, when he had visited that street. Nor had he noticed a shop called Costigans, yet here it now stood, and he was sheltering under its canvas rain cover. Smith then witnessed an amazing mirage-like vision.

As he glanced down the long road which now cuts through the area, he saw the houses and shops of the old 'Scottie Road' appearing, one after the other, from the morning mist. It was a breathtaking sight, which both alarmed him and yet, at the same time, filled him with nostalgic euphoria. A deeply satisfying sense of 'coming home' filled Mr Smith's very soul, and he beamed an inane smile at the phantoms of yesterday – people of the 1950s – who walked by, suspiciously silent. He somehow suspected that the incredible scene before him would vanish like a burst soap bubble if he started to doubt his senses, and he continued on down the street, struggling to keep his disbelief at bay, but the rational part of his mind kept reasserting itself, and eventually got the upper hand. The old voice of scepticism – 'This can't be happening' – nagged inside his head, and sure enough, the vibrant, bustling scene around him slowly evaporated, along with the heavy dew of that summer's morning.

Smith turned around and retraced his steps, desperately hoping that he would be able to recapture once again that favourite time of his life, but he could see nothing but the desolate Scotland Road of today; in places greened over and in others virtually obliterated by concrete and tarmac carriageways. Smith sighed as he was forced to accept the stark fact that the wonderful old neighbourhood of his childhood had been reduced to nothing more than a place you passed through on your way to somewhere else, and it left him feeling empty and consumed with despair.

The timeslip experience deeply affected Smith. He could no longer find fulfilment in the present, no matter how hard he tried, and in an effort to try and recapture some element of what he had lost, he ploughed a great deal of his wealth into a bizarre personal project which convinced his brother that he had suffered a nervous breakdown. Smith bought the premises of a closed-down factory near Speke, and set about hiring a small army of joiners, plumbers, electricians and scenery experts from the theatre to reconstruct the inside of his old home, just as it had been, on Scotland Road.

The end result was a strange mock-up of a 1950s home with two upstairs rooms, a back and front parlour, and a kitchen. The black and white television was wired to a video player loaded with television programmes from the 1950s, and the radio was hooked up to a long-playing tape, featuring period pieces like *Hancock's Half Hour, The Clitheroe Kid, Journey Into Space,* and *PC 49*, as well as all of the musical hits of the period.

When Smith looked out of the bay windows of his ersatz home, he saw an exact replica of the scene on Scotland Road that he had seen from his real childhood home; the scenery had been created by artists and photographers using old photographs borrowed from the City Engineer's collection.

Smith spent more and more of his time at the reconstructed house near Speke, and would give specific instructions to his brother and business acquaintances that, during his 'stay-overs' at the factory, he was not to be disturbed by anyone, or contacted on his mobile phone, unless it was a matter of the utmost urgency.

In the following year, Smith's brother went to visit relatives in Australia, and when he returned a month later he tried repeatedly to get in touch with his brother, but with no success. In the end he contacted the police and told them about the 'house' at the factory. The police went to investigate and found Mr Smith's body in the parlour of the simulated house of the past. He was lying dead in an armchair with a reprint of a 1950s *Evening Express* spread out on his lap. The body had obviously lain there for quite some time, filling the room with a stomach-churning odour. It was established by autopsy that death had been from a massive heart attack, and had probably been instantaneous.

After the funeral, Smith's brother had the fake house torn down.

This story is just another strange episode in the history of Liverpool.

WATCH THE BEDBUGS DON'T BITE!

A t a certain house somewhere in Liverpool, in 1999, a man named Andrew Gill got into bed one night at around midnight. He turned off the bedside lamp, and was drifting off to sleep, when he distinctly felt the blankets to his left slowly lifting, letting in a cold draught. Something small and ice-cold then slipped into bed next to him and Mr Gill held his breath, petrified. The 'thing' snuggled down next to him and started making a peculiar whimpering sound – like a child who was upset. Something freezing cold then brushed past his left ear, and so Mr Gill slowly turned, hardly daring to look, to find a small bony hand – the size of a child's – gently touching his ear. Then he heard a repulsive gurgling sound, and he glanced over to his right. What he saw would send him running out of the bedroom in his underpants.

A grisly-looking child of about six years of age was resting next to him, and by the light from the lamp-post filtering into the room, Andrew could see that the child was grossly decomposed – almost skeletal – and bubbling through a wide gash in its throat was blood, masses of blood.

Andrew can't remember actually leaving the bed. All he recalls next is hurtling headlong down the stairs in the dark, rendered speechless by what he had just experienced. He quickly scrambled into his clothes and fled to his friend's house. Andrew and his friend Jonathan, had known each other since they were children, and as soon as Jonathan saw him he was in no doubt that something terrible had happened and he invited him to spend the rest of the night at his house, an offer which was gratefully accepted.

The next day, the two men ventured back to the house together, and even in broad daylight, there was an eerie, almost tangible, atmosphere about the place, as soon as they walked in the door. The bedroom was now empty, but a peculiar smell hung thickly in the air. Andrew had been so spooked by the experience that he refused to stay there on the following night, and Jonathan suggested swapping houses for a week. Jonathan had read all of my *Haunted Liverpool* books and had always wanted to be a ghost hunter, so it seemed that the perfect opportunity had presented itself and he was therefore eager to exchange places with his friend. Andrew had lived at the house for over five years and had never experienced anything strange before, which deepened the mystery.

On the following night, Jonathan set up a night vision camera on a tripod, and directed it at the bed. He adjusted the timer to set the camera in motion at 1am, before climbing into bed full of excitement and expectation. Despite this he slept soundly in that bed that night. Nothing happened. Jonathan was undeterred, determined to share the same experience as Andrew and he kept the camera set up for a few more nights.

On the third night, he woke up abruptly at 2.30am, to find that he was covered in red spots all over his arms, chest and abdomen. The deep, ruby red spots were even all over his genitals. Suspicious, Jonathan then played the footage which had been recorded that night by the night vision camera. For a long time all that could be seen was his sleeping form huddled beneath the blankets. Then, suddenly, he saw the edge of the blankets slowly crawl towards his inert body. The edges of the sheets rolled back, and for a split-second, what seemed to be a skull-like face came into focus and stared into the camera before vanishing. Then Jonathan watched in horror as black spots crawled over the headboard and inched their way across his pillow towards his sleeping face. More black spots were crawling across the white sheets covering the mattress. They crawled under the sheets – always in his direction – and they were soon swarming all over him. Jonathan fast-fowarded the footage, and he saw the black bugs retreating back to the place from which they had come, as his body squirmed about under the covers. At this point he began to feel decidedly uncomfortable; the idea of those filthy creatures crawling all over his body sickened him and he groped for the light switch and turned on the light. He then searched underneath the bed and thoroughly examined the walls, but he could see no bugs, nor any small cracks or crevices in which they might be hiding.

The only things he found under the bed were an adult magazine – and a small, grey, one-eyed teddy bear. As soon as he touched that bear he felt that there was something threatening and malign about it – something which he couldn't quite put his finger on. Then the bear moved – ever so slightly – but it moved. Jonathan froze, and knocked the bear out from under the bed with his fingertips. He picked it up and squeezed it slightly. It had a revolting, putrid aroma about it, like rotten meat. Jonathan then noticed that there was a small ragged tear in the bear's neck, and he pulled it open slightly, and found a cluster of small, ruby red berries inside it. One of these berries plopped out on to the palm of his hand, and as Jonathan lifted it up to his eyes to examine it, the 'berry' bit him! It felt like a sharp pin being driven into his palm. He soon realised that the berry was actually a large bedbug, gorged with blood – his blood – hence the dark red colouring. There were hundreds more of the loathesome insects swarming about inside that teddy bear – it was infested with the things – and only now could he see their mandible mouth-parts, and black spindly legs moving ever so slowly. Jonathan retched and flung the old teddy bear across the room and wiped the disgusting bedbug off his hand and stamped on it, leaving a red stain on the carpet.

Days later, back at his own house, he was forced to call the doctor out because he was so ill. The medical man told him that the bedbugs were gluttons, feeding machines who sucked as much blood out of their sleeping hosts as they could, after which they often became so bloated that they couldn't squeeze back into the nooks and crannies from which they'd come, so they had to wait until they could digest the blood by hiding under beds, out of sight.

Andrew was totally mystified by what his friend told him and he searched everywhere for the teddy bear, but he couldn't find it, and he swore that he had never owned such a musky old teddy bear. However, Andrew Gill's neighbour proved to be a mine of information about the house where the supernatural events had taken place. He revealed that the house had been haunted since the 1920s, and local legend had it that a woman had cut the throat of her young stepson after going insane. The name 'Seddon' was also seen to appear in the bathroom from time to time, and it was there that the child's throat was allegedly Apparently, the child had not died straight away, but had crawled away in agony and tried to hide in the bed of the same room where Andrew had felt the cold thing crawl in beside him. The neighbour revealed that the child's body was hidden under the bed for weeks, until the dreadful aroma of decomposition and the stepmother's increasingly psychotic behaviour alerted the authorities.

The ghostly child seems to go into hibernation for several years at a time, only to re-emerge and start haunting the house again with a vengeance every now and again.

Stranger still, the ghostly murdered child and the swarms of bloodsucking bugs were also said to haunt other bedrooms in the same street – could they be calling on your bedroom tonight?

THE WHISTLER

On Tuesday 11 May 2004, at around 11 o'clock at night, a woman in her sixties named Stella, was sitting up in bed, reading a book, unable to sleep. Her seventy-five-year-old husband Jeff was snoring loudly beside her, but Stella was enjoying a romantic novel by the light of her bedside lamp. It was a real page turner and she had just come to the most exciting part. She was determined to finish it before going to sleep.

The house where Stella and her husband lived was in the Cabbage Hall area of Liverpool, and the house was only about twenty years old. It had no history of ghosts, or hauntings, and Stella had never had a supernatural experience in her life. However, upon this Tuesday night, as Stella lay in bed reading, she suddenly stiffened – she had definitely heard a strange noise outside her door. It sounded like a floorboard creaking – as if someone was standing on the landing, right outside the bedroom door. Stella was gripped with fear and she let her book drop.

After about twenty seconds she gently tried to nudge Jeff awake. He didn't open his eyes, but grunted, "What?"

"Jeff, I'm sure I just heard a noise on the landing outside," she whispered. "Will you go and have a look?"

"The place is alarmed, for goodness sake," he grumbled bad temperedly. "How could anyone get in here? Don't be daft, Stella. Turn that light off and get some sleep."

"Great! Thanks a lot!" tutted Stella with disgust, as Jeff instantly fell fast asleep again.

She held her breath but the creakings had stopped and she tried to tell herself that she had just imagined them and presently went back to reading her book, but nevertheless kept casting nervous glances at the handle of the bedroom door. She could have sworn that it turned, but she couldn't be one hundred per cent sure by the dim light of the lamp.

Then, about two minutes afterwards, she heard a faint clang – as if someone was placing a pot or pan on the cooker. Stella put the book down and slowly crept over to the bedroom door, and listened. Her heart was drumming in her ears, but she could definitely hear someone rattling about downstairs in her home. The intruder was obviously deranged, or a drug addict perhaps, because he was whistling the famous Laurel and Hardy cuckoo theme at the top of his voice, alerting half the neighbourhood to his presence.

"This is it, I'm calling the police," Stella thought to herself.

She had left her mobile phone downstairs and she therefore hurried over to the bedside extension phone and dialled 999 – before she realised that the line had been cut downstairs, that is. She took a deep breath, and looked around for something she could use as a weapon. In a closet she found her husband's old golfing irons, so she grabbed hold of the heaviest one and practised wielding it. Looking back she didn't know what had come over her – she wasn't usually one for heroics – but she had decided to go downstairs and confront the burglar before he came upstairs and attacked her. She was more than ready to lash out at him with the golf club, she felt so angry and upset that her home had been violated by a stranger.

She was just about to leave the bedroom when the bedside lamp suddenly went out. Stella assumed that the oddball whistling burglar had flicked the mains switch off, so she threw the bedroom curtains wide open to let in the light from the lamp-post which was right outside the window. She then cautiously opened the bedroom door, just a crack at first. On the landing she saw something that was so utterly horrific and distressing, that it would cause her to move out of that house.

A small, grey-haired, old woman with a hunched back stood there, and Stella's attention was immediately drawn to the woman's face where one of her eyes was missing. Something glistened in the empty socket, which seemed to be brimming with blood. Then Stella noticed what she initially took to be a black thin choker around the old woman's neck, but this choker followed every contour of the veins and wrinkles in that scraggy neck. Stella squinted in the dark and realised that it wasn't a choker, but a deep gash in her throat. Someone had slit her throat from ear to ear.

In a pleading gesture, the old woman lifted her palm towards Stella, upon which Stella slammed the door in her face and scuttled back to the safety of her bed. She could still hear the creaking sound outside the door, so she dived under the blankets and shook Jeff awake. When he heard what was happening he was naturally a bit confused and kept telling Stella to call the police, even though she had told him the line had been cut. Stella groped her way out of bed in the darkness, expecting to find that the old woman had entered the room – but she wasn't there.

Stella then had an idea. Grabbing an ashtray from the bedside cabinet, she flung open the bedroom window, and aimed the ashtray at her neighbour's car, which was parked in the driveway next door. The ashtray ricocheted off the roof of the vehicle and set off the car alarm. Eventually the door opened next door and their neighbour Mark came running out in his tee shirt and boxer shorts to find out what was going on. Stella screamed down at him and told him what was happening.

"It's okay, Stella. I'll go and call the police. You just stay there," he called up to her.

After going back into his house to call the police, Mark came back out and tried Stella's front door – it was unlocked. He cautiously pushed the door wide open and went inside. The burglar had fled, but had taken with him a dvd player, dozens of dvds, a computer laptop, as well as money and other valuables. On the cooker, a large pan of water was furiously boiling away, and in the back of an armchair, the burglar had thrust a large carving knife, perhaps as a chilling warning of what he would have done to Stella if she had been foolish enough to come downstairs and confront him. The pan of boiling water would have been thrown in her face, as scalding is one of the vicious tactics employed by many burglars nowadays. How the criminal bypassed the alarm system was ingenious, but I'm not allowed to reveal that for obvious reasons.

Stella was not only devastated by the burglary, she was also badly shaken by what could only have been a ghost that she had seen outside her bedroom door – the ghastly apparition of the weird old woman with the missing eye and slashed throat. Stella wondered if that ghost had been trying to prevent her from going downstairs with the golf club to tackle the burglar. In other words, had she been trying to protect Stella? Even if the old woman's intentions had been benevolent, Stella knew that she could not live in a house which was haunted, and so she and Jeff were forced to move.

The identity of the apparition has not so far been established, but could quite possibly be the ghost of a murder victim from some incident way back in the past.

That is not quite the end of the story. A month after the burglary, Stella was boarding a bus at the Gyratory in Queen's Square in Liverpool, when a young voice behind her asked, "Have you got a light there, love?"

Without turning round, Stella said, "No, I certainly haven't. Smoking's not allowed on this bus."

The man let out a string of abuse, and managed to cadge a light from another passenger. As the bus accelerated away from the Gyratory, the man started to whistle loudly, much to the annoyance of the other passengers, who all exchanged irritated glances, but no one dared challenge him because it was obvious that he was not someone to be tangled with. For Stella, the tune was much more than an annoyance – she recognised it at once as the Laurel and Hardy cuckoo theme – the very same tune that the burglar had whistled in her house. Her blood turned to ice in her veins. The youth sniggered and increased the volume of his whistling, but Stella was too afraid to look round and confront him face to face. She scrutinised several young men as they passed her to get off the bus, but she couldn't be sure if the man she suspected of being the burglar was amongst them.

THE WHEEL OF LYONESSE

L egends of ancient submerged kingdoms and even entire sunken continents can be found across the world, and when one remembers that seventy per cent of the Earth's surface is covered by water, such legends are not surprising. Most of us are familiar with the legend of the lost continent of Atlantis, which, according to Plato, vanished overnight beneath the waters of the Atlantic around 10,500 BC.

It is also remarkable that, in no less than eighty-three countries, there are legends of a great deluge; a cataclysmic flood which completely covered all the low-lying land, taking every living creature with it. What is even more intriguing is that each of these ancient stories is very similar to the Biblical account of The Flood, with one man being given a prewarning of the impending catastrophe. In all of the different accounts the man saves himself and his family by either building a great ship, or climbing to the top of the highest mountain he could find.

~

Closer to home, we have the legendary tale of Kilgrimol, an island that once existed in the Irish Sea, a few miles off the coasts of Blackpool and Southport. It is said that the Kilgrimolians had become corrupt and indulged in shocking vices. Their whole social fabric was falling apart – feral children ran wild whilst their parents lay in drunken stupors, and idleness and infidelity were rife. Then, one year, during the winter solstice, terrible visions predicting the sinking of their island appeared in the skies above Kilgrimol at sunset.

A handful of sober individuals, led by a knight of good virtue, beheld the vision with terrible foreboding and immediately boarded a ferry to what is now Fleetwood. On the following day the skies over Kilgrimol turned as black as night and a tremendous storm broke over the island, with enormous hailstones, the size of hens' eggs, raining down on the terrified islanders. An impenetrable darkness cloaked the whole island. Kilgrimol then suddenly tilted to the west, before slowly sliding into the Irish Sea, drowning its entire population, as well as every other living creature. The bloated bodies of the islanders and their sheep, cattle and horses, as well as many wild animals, were washed up on the western shores of Lancashire for weeks afterwards.

Another legend of a drowned kingdom also has a local connection.

In 1899, a marine engineer from Aigburth named James Wylie gave a talk in a smokey, crowded room at Conway Place in Birkenhead on the subject of Lyonesse – a fabled land that once existed to the west of Land's End. Wylie claimed that he had recovered a number of ancient maps as well as other information about Lyonesse from an old Cornish fisherman named Trevenny. This legendary land was said to have linked Land's End with the Scilly Isles, and old Mr Travenny had come into possession of a map of Lyonesse and a strange cipher which showed the location of some ancient secret or mystery. Wylie's attention was immediately drawn by one of the names which featured in the cipher. The name was 'Merlyn' and Wylie was already aware of the fact that the sunken Island of Lyonesse had long been associated with King Arthur. Could this ancient document hold the clue to the mystery?

His interest whetted, Wylie enlisted the help of two associates and together they visited Trevenny at Land's End and within days the Liverpool engineer had successfully decoded the entire cipher. The information he gleaned led him to the mouth of a local cave which could only be accessed from a small, secluded beach where it stood right at the water's edge. The cave could only be entered at low tide because it became flooded at all other times and he was given a ride to the location in the local lifeboat.

After carefully consulting the tide tables and the lifeboatman, Wylie set off to explore the cave, trembling with anticipation at what great mysteries he might uncover. A small crowd of onlookers had also arrived at the mouth of the cave, having come in an assortment of small boats. Having got wind of Wylie's intentions, they too were excited and eager to be the first to see whatever he might find.

They didn't have long to wait. After a brief interlude Wylie was seen to emerge from the entrance of the cave, slipping and stumbling over the seaweed-strewn rocks and in his hand clutching what looked like some kind of precious stone.

What happened next staggers belief, but was witnessed by all the onlookers who had followed him to the beach. At the same time as Wylie was making his way out of the cave, their attention was diverted to a huge rounded object which was beginning to emerge from the incoming waters. Wylie was at first oblivious to the object. He blinked and rubbed his eyes as they became accustomed to the daylight after the darkness of the cave and anyway, he only had eyes for one thing – the mysterious stone which he cradled in the palm of his hand. Only when the shouts and cries of alarm from the crowd filtered into his brain was he alerted to the thing approaching from the sea. It looked like a massive millstone – but it was moving, and moving very fast – unmistakeably in the direction of Wylie!

The object chased Wylie along the beach, thundering along, propelled by some unseen force. It crushed all obstacles in its path, reducing the lifeboat which Wylie had used to access the cave to matchwood. As it rolled relentlessly onwards the two other men who had accompanied Wylie hid amongst the rocks, petrified by the sight of the strange gargantuan wheel, which was covered with a mantle of seaweed and barnacles and glistened as it hurtled towards its prey.

As the stone disc closed in on Wylie, his instincts screamed at him to throw the stone back into the sea. His instincts were right because the instant he did this, the wheel slackened its pace, turned, and then rolled off back into the sea, where it disappeared beneath the crashing waves.

After a year or two, as the memory of his terrifying encounter gradually began to fade, James Wylie's natural curiosity again got the better of him. He regretted having thrown away the stone before he could examine it properly and he decided that he would go back to the beach and search for it. For many years he combed every inch of that beach and the cave in the quest for that stone, but without success.

Could that wheel have been some magical sentry guarding Merlin's secret cave? We will probably never know.

FAMILY OF WEREWOLVES

In the winter of 1470, as the Wars of the Roses raged across the land, a very strange incident took place in the western extremities of the Forest of Bowland, in Lancashire. An enormous ravenous creature, said to be a werewolf, was at large in the area and it attacked and killed a miller and his wife, leaving what remained of their bodies in shreds.

Two soldiers were dispatched to investigate the horrific slaying and soon found a trail of blood which led them into a clearing deep inside the Forest of Bowland. In the clearing were two young children, both male, and aged about eight months and two years of age. They lay on the freezing ground, unconscious, with bite marks all over their bodies, but they were otherwise unharmed.

The soldiers exchanged anxious glances – they were both convinced that the children had also been attacked by the werewolf and their instincts told them to leave them where they lay. In the end they decided that they couldn't just abandon the children there, they were also victims, after all – and so they lifted them on to their horses and took them to nearby Whalley Abbey with the intention of handing over responsibility for them to the monks. One of the Cistercian monks took charge of the children and took them to the infirmary where he prepared to treat their injuries, but the soldiers warned him off. One of the soldiers said that the infant and young child must be killed, for they had been bitten by the werewolf, and so would be transformed into bloodthirsty werewolves themselves after nightfall. So they snatched the still unconscious children from the monk and fled from the monastery on horseback.

They set their horses to the gallop and rode until they had arrived at the deepest part of the forest. The soldiers dismounted, each clutching his pathetic human bundle under his arm. They gently placed the children side by side on the frosty, leaf-strewn ground and drew their swords. However, the soldiers were suddenly stricken by another crisis of conscience – they weren't used to this type of moral dilemma, their lives were usually black and white – and they couldn't bring themselves to kill the children. They would surely die anyway, they argued; it was freezing cold and there was neither food nor shelter for miles around. So they covered them with a blanket of leaves, leaving just their heads showing, and quickly remounted their steeds and rode away.

Someone must have rescued these children – perhaps some woodcutter, farmer, or charcoal burner – because years later there came reports of two brothers, one with fiery red hair, and the other with raven-black hair, who roamed the area at night, transformed into werewolves. One of the wolves was red-haired and the other one was as black as coal from its pointed snout to the tip of its long bushy tail. The rising of a full moon acted as some kind of catalyst, and cause both brothers to exhibit prominent goose-pimples all over their bodies – the sure mark of a lycanthrope and the signal that they were about to undergo their terrible metamorphosis.

A beautiful local maiden named Miranda had the misfortune to become the object of the affections of both the accursed brothers, and, one hot and humid evening in the summer of 1487, she crept out of the village and made her way to a lake near the forest's edge. There she stripped naked and walked into the cool, green waters of the lake. The water felt delicious. She swam languidly around for a while then floated on her back watching the stars come out one by one in the twilight and the full moon passing in and out of the mist.

A noise, like the growling of a dog, only louder, suddenly roused her from her reverie and she stood upright in the water realising that she had left it rather late and that she had better make her way back to the village before darkness fell. As she waded to the shore the full moon once more broke through the clouds, illuminating the shoreline, where she was horrified to see two gigantic werewolves picking over her clothes with their great, slavering mouths where she had left them by some bushes. The creatures then began to fight with one another, snapping and snarling in their efforts to wrest the clothes from each other's grasp.

As the mighty beasts played out their deadly tug of war, Miranda silently slipped back into the water and attempted to swim away to the far shore, but when she was only about a third of the way across, her limbs suddenly turned to lead, as exhaustion overcame her. Normally a strong swimmer, she felt all her energy draining away. The cool water now felt thick and viscous and she started to drown, and quickly blacked out.

When she came to she found herself in her father's barn, naked, and covered in dried blood. Lying beside her in the hay was a red-haired youth with deep, livid red clawmarks gouged into his back. Miranda was confused and scared and tried to hide her nakedness with the hay. Presently her father came into the barn – a farmer named Slaidburn – and reassured her that all was well. He later revealed a breathtaking truth to the girl. The boy beside her in the barn, whose name apparently was Joshua, was not only her brother, but was also a werewolf, as was his younger brother Daniel.

His most startling revelation was that Miranda too was such a creature, but had yet to realise it. It was she who had inflicted the terrible clawmarks on Joshua's back the night before. She would have surely died from exhaustion in the lake if not for the incredible metamorphosis which had taken place – as her body had metamorphosed into its massive werewolf form. In doing so, it had gained superhuman strength and had been able to extricate itself from the life-threatening situation. Having done so it then returned to the warring werewolves on the other shore and attacked one of them, which later turned out to be her foster brother, Joshua.

The full story later unfolded. It was Farmer Slaidburn who had discovered the abandoned children Joshua and Daniel in the forest when he was out searching for his lost sheep, and he had wrapped them in a sheepskin and taken them back to his wife. He and his wife were unable to have children of their own and they were delighted to be able to create an instant family for themselves. Even after they had realised that the foundlings were werewolves, they had raised them as if they were their own flesh and blood.

On the day after the two brothers were rescued, a girl child was found, deep in the forest, close to the lair of the werewolf. Farmer Slaidburn rescued the child and called her Miranda. She would be a lovely sister for the two boys and make their little family complete. His wife was equally delighted.

Miranda never married, and lived to be almost one hundred years old. Her brothers, on the other hand, were said to have fathered many children, and fortunately, over the generations, the werewolf affliction became very much diluted in their descendants.

Have you examined your family tree lately? Perhaps the blood of the werewolf even runs in your own veins ...

FOG

The winter that stretched from December 1962 to March 1963 was one of the most severe on record. No place between John O'Groats and the Channel Islands escaped the freezing fog, followed by raging blizzards which blocked roads and railtracks, downed power and telephone lines, and cut off entire communities from the rest of the country. Even the sea itself froze in the subzero weather, leaving the country surrounded by a half mile coastal crust of ice. Both the River Thames and the Mersey also froze over, with night-time temperatures plummeting to minus sixteen degrees centigrade. The country's wildlife suffered very badly with birds doing worst of all. They fell down dead from their perches and died in their nests from the intense cold and starvation.

As Mark Twain once quipped, "Everybody talks about the weather, but no one does anything about it." Our transport system is rarely prepared for the variations in temperature which we experience in this country – in autumn the wrong sort of leaves on the line can bring the railways to a halt, and an icy patch, which is a guaranteed feature of every winter, can bring gridlock to the roads. I have often wondered about the feasibility of having infra-red heating elements built into lamp-post reflectors, to gently warm the roads with their fake sunshine whenever they are slicked with black ice.

In February 1963 there was a short but welcome lull in the glacial cold spell, which brought brief sunny mornings – a godsend to the weather-beaten people of the North West, but the price which had to be paid for these precious hours of golden sunshine came in the form of dense afternoon fogs, which rolled in from the Irish Sea and brought visibility down to almost nothing.

On one such miserable February afternoon of that year, thirteen-year-old Angus Pike, and a boy of identical age named Jack Robbins, uncharacteristically decided to play truant from school and ended up hanging around at the Pier Head for want of something better to do. They had enjoyed the morning with the bright sunshine but had then been plunged into a dull grey Limbo as the thick fog drifted in from Liverpool Bay. Angus had just enjoyed a mug of hot chicken soup at the Pier Head Café, which had temporarily provided him with some warmth, and Jack put on a scarf and a balaclava to keep out the damp cold air which the fog brought with it.

After spotting the silhouette of a policeman walking his waterfront beat, Angus and Jack quickly scurried away from the Landing Stage and melted into the fog. They knew that their school blazers advertised the fact that they were playing truant from school and they didn't want a confrontation. Soon, they could make out nothing in the fog but each other. The magnificent waterfront buildings and the ferries plying to and fro across the Mersey had all been enveloped by the fog and when they looked at each other their forms looked like ghostly silhouettes.

They edged their way cautiously along the riverfront and somewhere close to the Princes Dock, Jack Robbins spied a break in the safety chains, which was fortunate, for down below, directly in front of him, could be heard the swirling sounds of the river slushing against the sea wall. Then he noticed a rope bridge over to his right. It had wooden slatted footways that stretched out into the fog, fading into nothingness. Angus imagined that the bridge must lead to a ship, and he started to walk across it. The bridge swayed and wobbled as he walked and he gripped the handrail tightly. Having nothing to focus on made him feel dizzy and disorientated.

"Come on, mate," he shouted to Angus, a slight catch in his voice betraying his growing unease. "This is really cool."

"No, you've no idea where it goes. It might be dangerous. Come back here before somebody sees you."

So Jack remained where he was and watched as Angus's ghostly shape become fainter and fainter, before vanishing altogether. Then came a blood-curdling scream, and the rope bridge began to tremble violently. Jack called out to Angus, but there was no reply, just the sounds of the murky waters of the Mersey lapping against the sea wall, somewhere far beneath him.

Jack ran off into the fog and somehow managed to locate the policeman they had seen earlier. He stammered out what had happened to his friend and they both set off in search of the rope bridge. Jack tried to retrace his steps, which wasn't easy in the thick mist, but he was able to use the riverside as a guide. However, this time he could find no break in the safety railings, and no rope bridge either. Then, suddenly, they heard a boy crying, and the sound led them straight to Angus, who was found sobbing, minus his school blazer, wandering along the promenade in a daze.

The policeman set about trying to question the boy about what had happened to him and he gave a garbled account of a strangely-dressed man who had tried to keep him onboard a ship against his wishes. Angus had only managed to escape from his clutches by slipping out of his blazer, leaving the man clutching the empty garment.

After giving the boys a lecture about the dangers of playing truant and the importance of their education, the policeman gave them their bus fare home and told them to go home immediately without talking to anyone on the way.

Once he had seen them safely on to the bus the policeman resumed his beat. He was intrigued by the baffling incident, because it wasn't the first time he had heard about the phantom rope bridge. On numerous occasions people had come up to him on his beat with a very similar story. The bridge was said to appear whenever a dense fog blanketed the river, but as to who the would-be abductor was, and exactly *what* he was, for that matter, the policeman did not dwell upon for too long.

~

There have been many sightings of phantom ships – even of a ghostly liner – down at Liverpool Docks, and as recently as summer 2005, a security guard and two independent witnesses living in the flats overlooking the Albert Dock area, reported seeing the black silhouette of a liner floating on the river, moored near to the Landing Stage. The magnificent vessel was there at sunset, plain for all to see, and minutes later, it had vanished.

At around the same time, in 2005, a woman who runs a shop at the Albert Dock shopping complex was locking up late one rainy evening, when she caught sight of an old-fashioned caped policeman with a prominent walrus moustache, walking towards her. The outdated-looking officer of the law nodded to the intrigued woman, then proceeded on towards the Colonnades, where he seemed to melt into the darkness.

The shopkeeper was so spooked by this ghostly visitation that she called her sister on her mobile phone to tell her about the encounter. The woman's sister advised her to go and search for the phantom policeman, and to take a picture of him with the camera on her mobile phone. Instead, the shopkeeper hurried to the carpark, jumped into her car, and drove off home!

OUR HAUNTED ROADS

I have written about ghosts of the road in my books before, and here are a few more tales that have come to light. One dark morning in December 1997, at around 7.20am, a reader named Ray was driving up Bentley Road, off Lodge Lane, when he was intrigued to see a Morris Minor, in almost perfect condition coming towards him from the opposite direction. Another vintage car was following close behind the Morris Minor, but Ray is unsure of the exact make or model, but it definitely looked like a car from the 1950s or 1960s.

On the following morning, at approximately the same time, Ray was once again driving down Bentley Road, when the Morris Minor and another old-fashioned car approached and then passed him. Well, you might think, there is nothing particularly odd about that; lots of people drive pristine models of classic cars from decades ago, and they belong to organisations which stage various vintage car events and rallies. However, over the years, I have had a large number of telephone calls, emails and letters from people who have encountered a ghostly Austin 1100 and a Morris Minor, all in the vicinity of Bentley Road and Lodge Lane.

The earliest incident in my files took place on Tuesday, 19 August 1986, when forty-five-year-old Steve Jones was driving up Tunnel Road towards

Lodge Lane, on his way home from his brother's house. The time was 11.30pm and getting dark. He drove through the lights at the junction of Smithdown Road and Upper Parliament Street, and was heading for Lodge Lane, when a Morris Minor came out of Beaumont Street on the right, and slowly crossed the road towards Yanwath Street, coming directly into the path of Steve's car. Steve braked hard and then braced himself for the crash that he thought was inevitable. His white knuckles gripped the steering wheel as the Morris Minor loomed in front of him. However, incredibly, there was no impact, no clashing or tearing of metal or breaking of bones. Steve and his car passed silently straight through the rear end of the Morris Minor, as if it wasn't there.

A couple of men who had been drinking in the nearby pub, The Rob Roy, witnessed this astonishing spectacle from start to finish, having been initially alerted by the screech of Steve's brakes. As they ran out of the pub to help Steve, who was just as shocked as he would have been had there been a crash, they watched in disbelief as the Morris Minor just faded away in Yanwath Street, until only its red indicators could be seen; then they too winked off.

Steve Jones was convinced that he had hit the car, and, shaking violently, he staggered out and inspected his vehicle, expecting to find substantial damage, but there was none. The bodywork was in perfect condition except for the odd scratch which had already been there. As the two drinkers ran over from The Rob Roy, Steve too looked down Yanwath Street and watched as the ghostly car and its reckless driver faded away into the twilight.

The same ghostly Morris Minor was seen sometime afterwards on Croxteth Road, at the other end of Lodge Lane. This time it was endangering the lives of other motorists as it jumped the traffic lights, again during the hours of dusk, and on this occasion witnesses claimed that there appeared to be no driver at the wheel of the vehicle.

The incidents involving the phantom car are apparently still ongoing, and are one just example of the strange phenomenon of soulless ghosts – spectres of inanimate objects.

~

In 1995, a private hire taxi driver named Frank was driving his vehicle up Thomas Lane in Knotty Ash in the early hours of the morning, when he beheld a sinister and alarming sight on the road ahead. A series of cracks began to appear in the tarmacadam surface of the road, as if some silent earthquake was in progress. He drove on gingerly, understandably in a highly nervous state. He picked his way as best he could between the cracks, expecting his taxi and himself to fall into a yawning chasm at any minute, but the road felt perfectly smooth as he travelled along, and when Frank looked back, he noticed that the road surface of Thomas Lane was intact again. There wasn't a single crack in sight.

Like most supernatural goings-on on the highways and lanes of the North West, the origin and significance of this baffling road mirage is unknown.

~

The Phantom Arm of the Dock Road is another baffling apparition which confounds students of the paranormal.

Over the years, ranging from the mid-1990s to the present day, five different taxi drivers have contacted me to tell me about a disembodied human arm which they have seen reaching for the door handles of their cabs in the Strand area of Liverpool. All of these incidents have taken place in the winter months, and they are always at night.

The most dramatic of these encounters with the arm took place one December night in 2002 near Cooper's Emporium on the Strand. The time was close upon 11pm, and a hackney cab driver was waiting with his engine running to keep warm. He was expecting to pick up a woman who had phoned for a taxi earlier in the evening, but there was no sign of her. As the cab driver Jimmy impatiently drummed his fingers on the steering wheel, he happened to glance in his rear view mirror and noticed an arm reaching for the offside door handle of his cab. Jimmy turned round to check if it was the woman who had telephoned for his cab – when he froze.

It wasn't the woman, in fact it wasn't a person at all. Instead, all he could see was a male hand resting on the window pane of the door. The hand protruded from a grey sleeve, but that grey arm had no body attached to it. Jimmy slammed the cab into first gear and drove off like a bat out of Hell.

What Jimmy did not know was that he was the fourth cab driver to my knowledge to have had the misfortune to encounter the detached arm. Three other cabbies had already told me that they had come across the same grey arm reaching for the door-handles of their taxis.

The first of these weird incidents took place on the Strand in January 1995, around midnight, when a cab driver named Tommy was flagged down by a couple who had been caught in a sudden downpour. As the couple hurried through the rain from James Street towards the cab, with the man's coat over their heads, Tommy heard the door of his vehicle creak open, and turning around, he saw that the door was ajar, and that a man's fingers were curled around the edge of the door. The arm leading from the hand was clearly visible, but it had no body attached to it. Tommy was more astounded than scared, and watched, open-mouthed. The couple finally reached the taxi, unaware of the spooky event that was taking place, and as they went round the other side of the cab, the other door slammed, and the arm vanished.

The last sighting of the arm was on a rainy February evening in 2005, and was witnessed by two cab drivers who were waiting outside James Street Railway Station. The arm looked transparent on this occasion, and was seen to try the two doors of both parked cabs before vanishing back into the night.

Just whose phantom arm it is, and why it tries the handles of the taxis is unknown.

~

One of the most frightening incidents that has ever unfolded on the roads of Liverpool took place in the 1970s, in the aftermath of an horrific car crash. The smash-up took place when a stolen car which had been pursued by the police crashed in Netherley. The driver of the stolen vehicle, a man we shall simply call Mr Johnson, was a middle-aged petty thief, who was already well-known to the local constabulary. Johnson was thrown through the windscreen of the stolen car when it crashed into a Ford Cortina. Johnson's neck was broken in the impact and he died instantly.

All the other emergency services quickly arrived at the scene. The ambulancemen found a bloodstained, hysterical mother huddled beside the smouldering wreckage of her car, cradling her five-year-old daughter Ann-Marie in her arms. Mother and child had been in the Cortina, and the paramedics set about giving them emergency treatment on the spot. Little Ann-Marie's body was limp and her face totally lifeless, and the paramedics soon established that she had swallowed her own tongue. Having freed her airways, they were then able to resuscitate the child. Both the paramedics and the child's mother breathed an enormous sigh of relief as she spluttered back to life and drew in a deep, hungry lungful of air.

However, when Ann-Marie finally opened her eyes, her angelic features underwent the most disturbing metamorphosis. Her pretty face contorted into an expression of pure hatred. Then the child started to speak in an alien voice which sounded like that of an aggressive, adult male. She bared her teeth and uttered a string of shocking obscenities which again made her mother hysterical. All her invective was aimed at the policeman who had chased the stolen car. The child then passed out again and was quickly taken to hospital, where she later made a complete recovery.

The policeman who had been the object of the child's shocking verbal assault claimed that the voice was unmistakably that of Johnson, the thief who had perished in the car crash. Had Johnson's spirit somehow momentarily possessed the body of that inert child in a bid to vent his anger at the person whom he deemed responsible for his death? Nobody could be sure of exactly what had happened, but even the rational ambulancemen, the other hard-bitten police officers, not to mention the girl's bewildered mother, had to acknowledge that something truly sinister had taken place that day.

DEADLY SECRET AT THE STINGO

The following story was told to me several years ago, and, upon first hearing it, I was very dubious about its authenticity, until I researched the tale myself. I contacted those people who were involved, and soon came to realise that something sinister did indeed take place in 1960s Liverpool. Something which defies rational explanation.

In 1961, thirty-four-year-old Harry Turnbull was working for Martindale's Coal Merchants. One November afternoon, after Harry had delivered coal to various houses on High Park Street, Toxteth, he and his friend Davy Rankin went for a 'couple of swift halves of bitter' at a local public house called the Old Stingo. As the men warmed themselves by the blazing coal fire in the parlour, a local pensioner was annoying the 'coal porters' with a rather gloomy prediction. Ted Bunbury, aged seventy-four, held up a small lump of smouldering coal which he had picked up from the fire with a pair of tongs, and said: "Coal is prehistoric, and in a few years no house or factory shall use this stuff; nuclear power will take over."

"Oh put a sock in it, will you?" Harry muttered, leaning on the counter in the parlour, trying to block out the old prophet's ludicrous predictions.

"Pity you won't be around to see all this come to pass then, Ted," Davy

Rankin cruelly remarked to the old freethinker.

Ted Bunbury threw the coal back into the flames, laid the tongs down beside the cast-iron fire surround, then approached the two coalmen. He picked up Harry Turnbull's half-pint glass of bitter from the counter and said: "If all of the liquid in this glass could be converted directly into energy, it would produce an amount equivalent to the muscular energy expended in an entire day by the world's population. If we could convert half a pint of liquid entirely into energy we could produce enough power to propel a spaceship the size of St Paul's Cathedral to the nearest star!"

Harry snatched the beer glass out the old man's hand.

"I wish you'd propel yourself out of here, you old fool," he said.

As Ted made his way back to his usual corner seat in a huff, Harry Turnbull spotted a beautiful looking girl of about seventeen or eighteen years of age, sitting at a table near the window. Although he realised she was only half his age, he started talking to her, and noted that she was drinking sarsaparilla. He bought her another glassfull of the cordial and brought his own drink to her table. The girl gave her name as Cathy, and she looked even more beautiful close to – large brown eyes, long black hair, and a fresh-complexioned face. Davy Rankin tried to talk his friend out of chatting up the girl because of her age, but Harry told him to mind his own business.

Just over thirty minutes later, Harry and Davy were due back on the coal wagon, and before they left, Harry asked Cathy to meet him again at the pub. The girl said she would call in at noon on Saturday.

On the day of their first date, Cathy was dressed in the height of fashion, and upon her head she wore a pillbox hat made from beaver fur fabric to defy the winter weather. Harry also looked suave in his well-cut Peter Pell tailored suit. The couple had a drink, then Harry took Cathy to Webb's Used Car Dealers in Berry Street. He had been looking at a cream 1959 Ford Zodiac for a few weeks now, and had finally decided to purchase it for five hundred and sixty-five pounds. Having bought the car, they cruised out of Liverpool in the Zodiac and ended up in a small cosy pub near Widnes. Harry sat with his arm around Cathy in an arched alcove at the old fashioned pub as they talked and talked. They told each other about their lives, and found that one thing they had in common was a longing to find that elusive someone who could give them love and security. Harry felt certain that Cathy was exactly the type of girl he had been waiting for, for so many years.

After some time, Cathy got up to go to the toilet, and Harry decided he would jokingly tell her that he had missed her when she returned – but Cathy didn't return. The minutes wore on, and there was still no sign of her. Harry ended up asking various women emerging from the ladies toilet if there was a girl of Cathy's description in there. They all replied in the negative and Harry was so puzzled and confused by the girl's disappearance, that he eventually barged into the toilets and had a look for himself. The pub landlord saw what was happening and seized the coalman's arm and asked him what his game was. Harry told him he couldn't find the girl he had come into the pub with, but the landlord told him he had seen no such girl. Harry pointed to the table in the alcove where he had spent an intimate evening with Cathy and saw that the glasses from which she had sipped her drinks had vanished, yet his own beer glasses, both empty and full, were still there. Harry then remembered the cigarettes that Cathy had smoked while in his company, but having examined all the cigarette butts in the ashtray he found none which bore any traces of lipstick.

Harry frantically drove round the area, in search of Cathy, and at one point beeped his horn at a girl on the road who was wearing a beaver fur pillbox hat – but when she turned round, Harry was disappointed to see she was not his sweetheart. Eventually, Harry gave up and despondently drove back to Liverpool. He recalled Cathy saying that she had lived somewhere on Elaine Street, in Toxteth, and so Harry called at every house on that short street, but no one had heard of Cathy. He even went to a police station and told them what had happened, but they told him there was nothing they could do if the missing girl's surname wasn't even known.

For weeks, Harry frequented the Old Stingo pub where he had first set eyes on Cathy, in the hope that he would see her again, but he never did. Davy told his friend that perhaps the girl had decided to leave him for some reason, and tried to console Harry by saying that other girls would come along. And, sure enough, on 31 December of that year – New Years Eve – at around 7pm, Harry and Davy were in another Toxteth pub, known as Poets Corner, on Park Hill Road, when a beautiful blonde woman of about thirty years of age walked into the premises. All the male heads turned when she entered, and she went straight to the bar to order a drink. Harry stood there, agape, overawed by her stunning looks and shapely figure. Davy nudged him with his elbow to break the spell, and whispered: "Go on then, what're you waiting for?"

Harry sidled up to the beauty and watched her put a cigarette in her mouth. She searched her handbag for a lighter, and, seizing the opportunity, Harry dipped his hand in his coat pocket and withdrew a lighter in one swift movement. He flicked the cap off, thumbed it, and held the naked flame to the tip of the woman's cigarette. She inhaled, the tip of the cigarette glowed, and she turned to shoot a sensual smile at Harry. The world seemed to stop turning in that moment. Harry had never seen anyone as beautiful as the woman standing before him. She perched elegantly on a bar stool, and after thanking the coalman for the light, she asked him what his name was. Harry told her, and she said he had the most interesting eyes she'd ever seen. It wasn't long before the two of them were chatting and drinking.

Davy Rankin also met a girl at the pub that evening named Anna, who lived on Marsh Lane, Bootle and was drinking with relatives from Park Road, and although she was nowhere near as beautiful as the woman with whom Harry was drinking, she had a great sense of humour and a bubbly personality. The blonde Harry had met was Simone White, and she lived in the Dingle. She was single, and had recently broken off an engagement because her fiancé had cheated on her. Almost five hours passed by in that pub until the clock approached midnight. Soon 1961 would be gone forever, and people were pouring out of the pub on to the chilly street outside, where they got ready to hold hands in a circle to sing Auld Lang Syne. Everyone waited as the hour hand crept to twelve, and suddenly in the hush, there came the sounds of the foghorns on the river, and the distant cheers of people across the neighbourhoods. Simone held Harry's hand and they linked up with the circle of revellers outside. Davy Rankin held hands with Anna, and also joined the circle. Everyone started to move in a clockwise direction and someone started to sing: 'Should auld acquaintance be forgot, And never brought to mind?'

The circle revolved, and Harry found himself singing as he looked up at the stars. All that drink and the intoxicating perfume of Simone made those stars swim about in the sky as he shuffled along in the circle, and when the song was done, he gazed sideways to the lovely Simone – and found her gone! In her place Harry Turnbull found he was clasping the hand of an old woman. He looked about confused, then released the old woman's hand. He broke up a passionate kiss that Davy and Anna were enjoying and asked his friend where Simone was.

"How the Hell should I know?" was Davy's indignant reply.

Harry searched every inch of the pub but the blonde woman was nowhere to be seen. He walked the streets of the area, looking for Simone, but it was as if she had vanished off the face of the earth – just as Cathy had done weeks before.

Harry awoke the following morning on Davy's sofa, and in the first minute of waking it felt as if Simone and her mysterious disappearance had been some kind of strange dream. As he struggled with a throbbing hangover, Harry asked Davy if he remembered Simone, and his friend said she was hard to forget, given her stunning face and figure. Harry told him about the way she had vanished, just like Cathy had, and in reply, Davy had joked, "You're cursed, mate."

Harry returned to the Poets Corner pub and made enquiries about Simone, but no one knew anything about her. In desperation, he drove round the Dingle area, hoping to spot the elusive blonde, but never set eyes on her again. Deep down, Harry felt as if there was something sinister, almost supernatural, about the two vanishing women. He was just a simple man, a coalman, yet he felt something – some higher intelligence – had been playing with him. It was difficult to put into words. Davy Rankin certainly didn't have any idea what he was getting at, but old Ted Bunbury, the man he had sneered at, might understand, Harry reasoned. He regretted mocking the intelligent old man who had talked about coal becoming superseded by nuclear power, and wondered if he might be able to throw any light on the mysterious disappearances of Cathy and Simone. Harry found the pensioner sitting on his own in the Old Stingo pub one quiet Sunday evening, and he bought him a drink. He told him what had happened in precise detail, then asked him if he could provide an explanation. The old man stared into the glass of stout, deep in contemplation, and after a tense pause he said:

"Shakespeare said, 'There are more things in Heaven and Earth than were dreamed off in our philosophy.' Have you ever heard that quote?" Harry shook his head. "Well, let me put it this way, son; the universe is a big place. Ever looked up at the stars at night?"

"Yes," replied Harry, thinking about that New Year's night, when he had watched the stars whirl about through a drunken, lovelorn haze.

Mr Bunbury sipped the tangy stout, smacked his lips, then reflected on the scale of the cosmos.

"Those stars are distant suns, believe it or not, like the sun we have in our sky down here, and all those billions of suns out there have planets circling around them, and God Himself only knows what beings live on those worlds. There might be beings out there who learned how to split the atom when the dinosaurs were still walking our world. They might be so advanced, they would regard us as either pests or playthings."

"I don't see what you're getting at," Harry admitted.

"Think of a rat in a maze," said the old man. "Behaviourologists study rats in mazes and note the way they react to certain stimuli, in order to fathom out how their minds tick. And for all we know, something up there might regard us in the same way, and they might toy with our lives, and play tricks on our minds, just to see how we react. Maybe that's why people see flying saucers and ghosts. Maybe some sort of mind manipulation experiment is going on."

"You're so wise," Harry told the old man with great sincerity. "I'm sorry for the way I talked to you in the past; it's all down to my ignorance."

The man appreciated the apology and offered to buy Harry a drink, but the coalman refused. Then Davy and Anna came into the pub, and Harry went over to sit with them.

"Were you drinking with Mr Brain's Trust then, Harry?" Davy asked, smirking at old Ted.

Harry said nothing, and asked Anna what she'd like to drink.

Almost an hour passed, and then Ted Bunbury came over to the table where Harry Turnbull was sitting with Davy and Anna. The old man looked as if he had something very important to tell Harry.

"I've just worked out what's going on, Harry, and it's incredible," said Ted, excitedly.

Harry's attention was instantly engaged.

"Hey, beat it old man," Davy told the pensioner, but Harry gestured for his friend to shut up and rose from the table, highly intrigued.

"You won't believe what those girls were," said Ted, looking wild-eyed, as if he had uncovered some great, yet dangerous, secret. The old man trembled and his bottom lip quivered. He had Harry's undivided attention now.

"What?" said Harry, impatiently waiting for an answer.

Then something invisible seemed to strike the old man in the back, winding him, and sending the bottom set of his dentures flying on to the table where Davy and Anna were seated. Mr Bunbury's eyes turned upwards until they were white, and his body started to crumple. Harry caught the old man, then cradled him in his arms. He didn't know what to do, and as Anna screamed, blood came trickling down Ted's nose, as a faint dribble at first, then as an alarming red gush which rapidly turned the old man's shirt scarlet. The barman came rushing over, and he felt Ted's neck for a carotid pulse, but found none. An ambulance was called for, and Ted Bunbury was pronounced dead on arrival at the hospital. The pensioner had suffered a massive cerebral haemorrhage after a blood vessel had burst in his brain. Death had been instantaneous.

Harry Turnbull didn't accept the official mundane explanation for the old man's sudden death. Something had definitely struck Mr Bunbury and sent his dentures flying out with the impact. Davy Rankin and Anna, as well as a handful of other drinkers at the pub, had seen and heard the effects of whatever it was that struck the old man. Harry was left with the terrifying impression that Ted had been struck down by something because he had been about to reveal some terrible secret connected with the girls who had come into his life so transiently.

Of course, it could all be a coincidence, and perhaps the girls simply left Harry for reasons known only to themselves, and he was merely unable to trace them. Harry however, thought differently, and believed Ted Bunbury had used his intellect to unravel some great mystery that should have been left alone; a dangerous secret which cost him his life.

MYSTERIOUS VISITORS

Mrs Jones remembers the evening vividly when the 'thing' looked through her window. It was just after 8.30pm on Friday, 16 September 1983. Mrs Jones had just made herself a cup of tea after watching an episode of the American television series, *The A-Team*. She settled back into her favourite armchair in the living room of her well-kept home on Roughwood Drive, Kirkby, enjoying the first few minutes of an ITV comedy called *The Bounder*, which starred Peter Bowles and George Cole. A flash of purplish light briefly illuminated the net curtains, and Mrs Jones assumed it was lightning. She waited for the rumble of thunder but none came. As she watched the television comedy something once again flashed outside her first floor window. This time a small red point of light, as bright as an LED indicator, seemed to hover outside the window, and the forty-five-year-old Kirkby housewife went to see what it was. She lifted the net curtain and looked out.

A globular object with a diameter of about six feet was levitating silently in front of her window, less than five feet away. A circular, silver-rimmed porthole was visible on the surface of the globe, and through a lens in the centre of the hole, a red light was winking. Mrs Jones felt as if something unearthly was watching her through the lens and she lowered the net curtain in shock, and ran out of her flat and hammered on the door of her neighbour, Mrs Johnson. It transpired that Mrs Johnson had seen something briefly pass by her own window earlier in the evening, but she had assumed it had been a child's balloon. Both women looked out of the window and could see no sign of the hovering globe with the red luminous eye.

However, during the following weeks, strange lights were seen in the skies over Kirkby, Melling and parts of Knowsley. A globe-shaped object, possibly the one that had been 'peeping' through Mrs Jones's window, was seen flying low over a house in Gillmoss and shining a high-powered beam of laser-like light on Knowsley Brook.

Seven years before, during the winter of 1976, officers at a Kirkby police station were bemused, then intrigued, when four local men gave themselves up after poaching on a remote farm near Melling. The men said they had witnessed the landing of a spaceship and had seen ghastly-looking, green-skinned beings emerging from the craft. The men were all stone cold sober and had not been taking drugs, yet all four poachers were in a state of nervous excitement, but the police who investigated the alleged landing of the spacecraft near the Melling farm could find no evidence to back up the incredible story.

Days after the alleged close encounter, strange lights were seen travelling in the starry skies over Melling Mount, and one local amateur astronomer tracked the unidentified luminous points as far as Lydiate, where they dispersed into different directions.

Nine years before, in the late summer of 1967, two schoolboys decided to camp out in woodland in the area of Gillmoss where the M57 Motorway now runs. They built a small fire, and set up a tent, but didn't get much sleep because they kept on hearing strange musical sounds which seemed to be coming from overhead. Then, at around three in the morning, they saw something dark and triangular passing by in the sky above. It blocked out the starlight and the glow of the Milky Way, then halted directly overhead. A metallic gong sound grew steadily louder in volume, and the schoolboys realised that the triangular object was descending on to them. The ground started to vibrate as a deep rumbling sound pulsated down from the object. The boys were so afraid that they ran screaming from the woods and all the way to their homes. One of the boys, named Michael, said that he looked back at one point and had seen freakishly tall figures standing in the woods, apparently watching him and his friend run off.

119

Throughout that year, unidentified flying objects had been seen throughout Europe, both day and night, prompting questions to be asked in the Commons about the matter. Locally, there were many spectacular sightings and encounters with things no scientist or astronomer has ever explained satisfactorily.

In July 1967, a car travelling along the East Lancashire Road at two o'clock in the morning was followed by a bright red light. The couple in the car, a man and woman in their thirties from Kirkby, actually felt the vehicle rise up from the road at one point as if some magnetic force, akin to the tractor-beam of science fiction, was sucking them up into the air. Luckily, the object put the car back down and sped off to the north.

Just what these UFOs are is anybody's guess, and where they come from remains a mystery. Are they visitors from any of the trillions of planets in our sector of the galaxy, or could they be from the past or future? Some ufologists even believe these mysterious visitors originate from somewhere close in a dimension that overlaps our own, but no one can be certain of their origins.

Several years ago in Croxteth, a child who attended Our Lady & St Swithins Primary School, saw a UFO in broad daylight, flying north over Parkstile Lane. No one believed the child, but one night the child's mother found him gazing out of his bedroom window. He had seen a bright blue light hovering over Randle's Bridge Farm, on the Knowsley and Liverpool border. She told him it was the police helicopter, but it wasn't, because the object flew vertically upwards at an incredible speed and not only did it do so silently, it ended up as a star-sized object, apparently miles above the ground. The child became fascinated with the luminous object, and whenever his friend stayed over, they would watch the skies from the bedroom window with a pair of low-powered 8x30 binoculars.

One night, in the summer of 2002, the boys opened the window at around midnight, and saw that a bright, flare-like object was hovering over Craven Wood, about half a mile distant. The object dimmed, and on several occasions, it shone beams of light at the young observers, as if it was trying to communicate. The object then left at high speed and vanished. The boys went back to bed, but at around three in the morning, screams echoed through the house in Croxteth. The mother and father ran upstairs to the room, and found the children crying in a corner. They said they had seen a 'scary face' on the wall of the bedroom. It's mouth was moving, and it looked as if it was speaking, but the eyes were huge, black and round. The parents said the boys had been seeing things, but they turned off the bedroom light, they too saw a strange luminous image on the wall. It was of a weird face with a mouth that opened and closed like a goldfish, and the eyes were black and disc-like. The father established that the face was being projected into the room through the window which the boys had left wide open. After the father broke the beam with his hand several times, the projected face vanished, never to return.

Was this sinister face projected via the beams of the UFO seen over Craven Wood? If it was, whose face was it? We may know more one day.

THE VAGRANT AND THE STARS

Charles Jevington was born in Aigburth around 1889, and at the age of twenty-five was almost fatally wounded in the trenches during World War One. His injuries were so serious that he was sent home immediately from the front, and within a week was being given the Last Rites by a priest. Somehow though, through sheer willpower, the appalling injury to his abdomen slowly began to heal, even though a Harley Street physician had forecast that the colon would soon begin to die because of gangrene. As the months went by, Jevington made a full recovery, baffling doctors and surgeons and convincing the family priest that a miracle had taken place.

However, a year after Charles had narrowly cheated death, his beloved wife died from breast cancer and the former soldier suffered a severe mental breakdown. Jevington dropped out of post-war society and became a vagrant. For a while he lived in Flint in North Wales, where he managed to drag himself out of the gutter for a while, working on a farm, then helping out at the local bakery. Somewhere along the line, Jevington reverted to his nomadic life as a vagabond and headed for the Lake District.

By the 1950s, Jevington was known as Old Charlie, a sixty-one-year-old tramp who survived on handouts from the charitable people of Thursby – a village on the outskirts of Carlisle. Charlie was a well-loved character amongst those simple rural folk, and was often seen in the corner of the local pub with his arthritic, limping old mongrel dog, Arthur.

In May 1955, a mystery unfolded in this pub which has never been satisfactorily explained. That month, old Charlie Jevington and his dog went missing. When the likeable vagrant and his hound weren't seen after three days, people became sufficiently concerned to notify the police, and it wasn't long before constables and locals were scouring the local woods and searching fields and hedgerows. Rivers were dragged and posters bearing an artist's impression of Jevington were posted in nearby villages. Jevington was known to have one relative in Liverpool – a cousin named Muriel Molyneux – so the police in Cumbria liaised with the Lancashire police, who sent officers to a house in Old Swan, where, alas, Mrs Molyneux had passed away three months previously. There, the search for Charles Jevington ended.

Then, five years later, in December 1960, events took a very sinister turn when Charles Jevington and his dog Arthur strolled into the pub at Thursby, and the tramp had an incredible tale to tell the amazed locals.

Charles Jevington explained his long absence by claiming he had been onboard a flying saucer for the past five years. He said that people from another planet had invited him and his dog on to their spaceship. The tramp was understandably nervous, but the people had such kind faces and seemed so non-threatening, that he accepted the invitation. That ship took Jevington on an incredible voyage across the galaxy to many weird and wonderful worlds. Most of the locals scoffed at such an apparently far-fetched yarn, but the barmaid of the pub pointed out that Charlie's dog, Arthur, didn't look a day older than when it had gone missing five years back, and, what's more, its limp had gone.

An amateur astronomer fired several questions at the vagrant in an effort to shoot holes in his fantastic tale. He posed technical questions about stars, planets, moons and nebulae, and Jevington not only answered these abstruse queries, but also revealed a fact that was years ahead of its time. The star-gazer asked the tramp if he had passed Saturn on the flying saucer, and Jevington answered that he had, and that he had also passed other planets further out than Saturn that also had rings around them.

"Ah you're wrong there, old man!" bellowed the amateur astronomer, and with a triumphant smile he started to light up his calabash.

"Why am I wrong, sir?" Jevington demanded to know.

After an exhalation of aromatic pipe-smoke, the enthusiast of the telescope answered: "Saturn is the only ringed planet in the Solar System. Get your facts straight before you make up this nonsense!"

The drinkers in the pub again started to doubt Jevington's incredible tale in the light of the glaring mistake he had made about ringed planets. The ridiculed tramp left the pub with Arthur. The last person to see the vagrant was an old blacksmith, and Jevington told him that his friends from space would be picking him up again at a prearranged rendezvous in a few weeks time.

A fortnight later, Old Charlie and his dog went missing again, and this time it was for good. Around the time of the disappearance, three farmers in the area saw a huge, disc-shaped UFO flying through the starry skies over Penrith.

Seventeen years later, in 1977, a NASA space probe discovered several dark ring systems around Jupiter and Neptune. These rings cannot be observed from Earth and were not even guessed at in 1960 – so how did Charles Jevington know about them? Was it all coincidence, or, are a tramp and his faithful dog somewhere out there in the depths of infinite space?

THEY CAME TO SAY GOODBYE

Here is just one of the many hundreds of letters I receive each year from the readers of my books and columns:

Dear Tom,

My name is George, I am fifty-two years of age, have three children and one grandson. Twelve years ago my grandson Ryan was born. Me and my partner Maria were at the hospital at the time of his birth, and over the two days after his birth we were back and forth between home and the hospital, and eventually took Ryan and his mother home to our flat on Laurel Road, Kensington. A few days after this, at around 5pm, I got out of my car outside the flat and looked up to the second floor bay window of the flat, and I saw a girl walk across the window inside the place. She had light hair and was wearing a school uniform.

I went up into the flat and saw Emma was washing her baby Ryan in his bath. I started looking for the little girl and realised she couldn't have possibly walked across the window because the leather couch was completely filling the recess of the bay window. Emma asked me what I was looking for, and when I told her she looked horrified, then told me that my niece had died a few hours ago, and that my son Lee had gone to her house. I know that the girl in the window I saw was my niece Debbie. She had been ill for seven years and had been having chemotherapy, which meant she also lost all of her hair for the whole period of her illness.

The school uniform I saw the little girl in was Debbie's uniform, and she had a full head of hair though, and looked in full health. I know it was her and that she had come to say goodbye to me. I haven't seen her since that day but because of that vision, she is still alive in my head and always will be.

Yours sincerely
George

George's touching story is a typical example of a loved one making a last visit to say farewell before he or she passes into the world of spirit.

~

In the 1970s, in the Page Moss district of Liverpool, a child of thirteen named Carl was sneaking into his father's bedroom one afternoon to steal bundles of Embassy cigarette vouchers. At the time, Carl's dad was at work, as were his mother and older sister. The house on Western Avenue was empty, and Carl should have been at school, but was playing truant. He planned to sell the cigarette vouchers to his friend's mother, as she had a gift catalogue from which she could exchange coupons for various items. Carl left his parents' room that afternoon and found his way barred by his grandmother.

"You've turned to robbing your own father now, have you?" she said, very sternly, standing before him with her arms crossed. Carl was baffled, because he had visited his gran in the Northern Hospital a few days ago, and he'd heard his tearful mother say her condition was deteriorating. Yet she looked as right as rain standing here in the hallway.

Carl put the coupons back and as he walked out of his parents' bedroom his gran hugged him, then told him to stop playing truant. Carl noticed that she had a tear in her eye, which was unusual, as she had never been a woman to show emotion. He left the house shame-faced at being caught red-handed, and later that day, he learned from his mother that his grandmother had passed away at eleven that morning, after suffering a major stroke. Carl insisted that he had seen his beloved gran in the afternoon, standing in the hallway, although he didn't admit that she had caught him stealing. Carl's parents said it was impossible, as his gran would have been dead by then, but the boy insisted that he had met her, and even today he believes she somehow visited him in spirit that afternoon, to stop him from becoming a criminal.

~

Many years ago, around the late 1980s, a ghostly incident, in which a deceased person said goodbye to his wife, took place at the Royal Liverpool University Hospital on Prescot Street. A man from Sheil Road named Jimmy Reide was dying from lung cancer and his health had gone into such a decline, that he was taken off the ward and put into a room by himself. Mrs Reide was allowed to sleep overnight at the hospital because the doctor had told her that Jimmy had just a few days left. Mrs Reide was herself a heavy smoker, and at this time the hospital had a smoking room where visitors – and some patients – went to smoke.

So, at around 8pm, Mrs Reide sat in the smoking room, gazing tearfully out of the windows at the incredible night-time views of Liverpool. Constellations of yellow sodium lamps dotted the nightscape outside, and, as it was Sunday, the city lights included the kaleidoscope of coloured windows glowing mystically in the upper reaches of the Metropolitan Cathedral. Mrs Reide inhaled her cigarette and watched the reflection of its incandescent tip grow to glowing prominence. A familiar figure came into view, reflected in the window. It was her husband, Jimmy. She spun around slack-jawed, stuck for words, unsure as to whether it was a cruel dream. He looked in the best of health, and that did not make sense, because she knew he was at death's door in the next room, weak as a kitten. He had been wired and plumbed to machines minutes ago, but now he stood there with a smile on his face.

"I love you, girl," he said, and his voice sounded young, the way it had sounded when they had been courting in Kensington all those years ago. He leaned over and threw his arms around his wife, so her face was buried in his chest. He hugged her the way he had hugged her that time when she had been young, when she had told him she was pregnant with their first child.

"Jim! Oh Jim!" Mrs Reide sobbed, and suddenly, there was nothing there. She looked up, and saw another stressed-out relative of some patient, entering the smoke room. She asked the man if he had just seen someone pass him on the way out. The man said no one had passed him. Mrs Reide hurried out of the smoke room as some dark intuition nagged at her. She tried to get into the room

125

where her husband was lying in his bed, but it was crowded with doctors and nurses and she knew it wasn't a good sign. A nurse told her that Jimmy was very close to death, and had lost all unconsciousness. A priest was at hand and asked Mrs Reide if she would like to say goodbye to her husband.

"No, Father. He just came to say goodbye, as true as God's in Heaven. He came into the smoke room and held me. Then he was gone."

She then turned back to the bed and watched as the nurse pulled the bedsheets over her dead husband.

~

The most intriguing and touching case of a post-death apparition took place in the 1950s at a house in Crosby.

Eleven-year-old Sally took the death of her beloved grandfather very badly, and one day, weeks after the death, she had been playing in her nursery when a music box started to play a tune which reminded her of her Grandad. She started to sob, but a familiar voice called out her name. Sally turned and through her tears saw that it was her grandfather. The child was not at all frightened and ran into his open arms. He carried her to the corner of the nursery and sat on a chair with her in his lap. He wiped the tears from her eyes and said he would always be around her. She asked him if he could come back to live with her and mummy and the rest of the family because she really missed him, and he said that he couldn't. He did, however, tell his granddaughter a touching tale, which she repeated almost word for word to her mother.

"Once upon a time, in a little pond, in the muddy water beneath a lily pad, there lived a tiny water beetle in a family of water beetles. They all lived a simple life in the pond, with few disturbances. But, every now and then, sadness would come to the family when one of their fellow beetles would climb the stem of a lily pad and never be seen again. They knew that once this happened, their friend was dead and gone forever.

"Then one day, one little water beetle decided to climb up that stem. However, the little beetle decided that he would not leave forever. He would come back and tell his friends what he had found at the top.

"However, when the little beetle reached the top and climbed out of the water on to the surface of the lily pad, he was so tired, and the sun felt so very warm, he had to take a nap. As the little beetle slept, his body started to change, and when he woke up, he had turned into a beautiful, blue-tailed dragonfly with broad wings and a slender body designed for flying. He flew up from the pond and saw the beauty of a whole new world, and a much lovelier life than any he had known. Then he remembered his beetle family and how by now they were probably thinking he was dead. He wanted to go back to tell them that he was now more alive than he had ever been before, but his new body would not let him go down under the water, so he couldn't get back to tell his family the good news. He felt sad for a while, but then he realised that their time would come. Then they, too, would fly up above the pond with him."

OTHER TITLES BY TOM SLEMEN

Haunted Cheshire	Tom Slemen	£5.99
Haunted Liverpool 1	Tom Slemen	£5.99
Haunted Liverpool 2	Tom Slemen	£5.99
Haunted Liverpool 3	Tom Slemen	£5.99
Haunted Liverpool 4	Tom Slemen	£5.99
Haunted Liverpool 5	Tom Slemen	£5.99
Haunted Liverpool 6	Tom Slemen	£5.99
Haunted Liverpool 7	Tom Slemen	£5.99
Haunted Liverpool 8	Tom Slemen	£5.99
Haunted Liverpool 9	Tom Slemen	£5.99
Haunted Liverpool 10	Tom Slemen	£5.99
Haunted Wirral	Tom Slemen	£5.99
Liverpool Ghost Walk	Tom Slemen	£5.99
Wicked Liverpool	Tom Slemen	£5.99
Haunted Liverpool, double cassette audio book, read by	Tom Slemen	£8.99

Available from all good bookshops
For a free stocklist contact
The Bluecoat Press, 19 Rodney Street, Liverpool L1 9EF
Telephone 01517072390

If you have had a paranormal encounter,
or a supernatural experience of any sort, please drop a line to:

Thomas Slemen
c/o The Bluecoat Press
19 Rodney Street
Liverpool L1 9EF

All correspondence will be answered.